First Edition

Common Core Support Coach

TARGET ➤ Foundational Mathematics 5

Dr. Jerry Kaplan
Senior Mathematics Consultant

Common Core Support Coach, Target: Foundational Mathematics, First Edition, Grade 5
T200NA   ISBN-13: 978-1-61997-976-5
Contributing Writers: Q2A/Bill Smith   **Cover Design:** Q2A/Bill Smith

Triumph Learning® 136 Madison Avenue, 7th Floor, New York, NY 10016

Contents

Analyzing Numerical Patterns

PLUG IN Number and Shape Patterns

A **rule** tells you how to get from one **term** to the next in a pattern.

This is a numerical pattern.

3, 6, 9, 12, 15

Each term in the pattern is 3 more than the term before it. The rule is *add 3*.

> Notice that the terms alternate between even numbers and odd numbers.

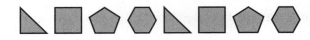

This is a shape pattern.

The rule is triangle, square, pentagon, hexagon.

> I can figure out the rule by looking at the shape of each figure in the pattern.

Words to Know

rule
tells how the numbers or figures in a pattern are related

4, 8, 12, 16, 20

The rule is *add 4*.

term
a number or figure in a pattern

4, 8, 12, 16, 20

The pattern has five terms.

DISCUSS When finding a rule for a numerical pattern, how do you know whether the rule is to add, to subtract, or to multiply?

A You can use a rule to create a number pattern.

DO Create the number pattern.
The first term is 3. The rule is *multiply by 2*.

1 Multiply the first term, 3, by 2 to find the second term.

_____3_____ × _____2_____ = _____

2 Multiply each term by 2 to find three more terms.

_____ × _____ = _____

_____ × _____ = _____

3 Write the five terms in the pattern.

_____ × _____ = _____

_____, _____, _____, _____, _____

4 Describe the terms in the pattern.

_____

B You can use a rule to create a shape pattern.

The pattern small triangle, large triangle, small square, large square repeats.

DO Create the shape pattern.
The rule is small triangle, large triangle, small square, large square.

1 Draw the first four figures in the pattern: a small triangle, a large triangle, a small square, and a large square.

2 Repeat the pattern.

△ ___ ___ ___ ___ ___ ___ ___ ___

3 Describe the terms in the pattern. Study the pattern.

_____

_____

_____

PRACTICE

Use the rule to complete the pattern. Then describe the terms in the pattern.

1 The rule is *add 5*.

10, __15__, _____, _____, _____

_____

_____

2 The rule is *subtract 4*.

30, _____, _____, _____, _____

_____

_____

3 The rule is *add 10*.

0, _____, _____, _____, _____

_____

_____

4 The rule is *multiply by 3*.

1, _____, _____, _____, _____

_____

_____

5 The rule is to add 3 squares to the top of the figure.

□□□ _____ _____ _____ _____

_____

A coordinate plane is a grid formed by a horizontal number line and a vertical number line. An **ordered pair** of numbers is used to name the location of a point on a coordinate plane.

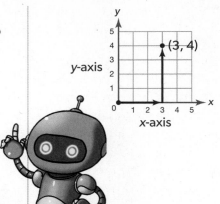

- The first number is the **x-coordinate**.
- The second number is the **y-coordinate**.
- The **origin** (0, 0) is the point where the x-axis and y-axis meet.
- To plot a point at (3, 4), start at the origin. Move 3 units to the right. Then move 4 units up. Draw a point and label the ordered pair.

> I see! The ordered pair (3, 4) lines up with 3 on the x-axis, and with 4 on the y-axis.

Words to Know	**ordered pair** two numbers that give a location on a coordinate plane (2, 3)	**x-coordinate** tells how many units to move to the right along the x-axis (2, 3)	**y-coordinate** tells how many units to move up along the y-axis (2, 3)	**origin** point located at (0, 0)

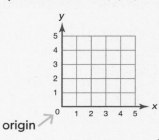

origin

DISCUSS Explain where the point (4, 1) would be located on a coordinate plane.

A You can use ordered pairs to plot a point on a coordinate plane.

DO Plot a point at (1, 6) on the coordinate plane.

1. Start at the origin.
2. Use the x-coordinate to move to the right.
3. Use the y-coordinate to move up.
4. Plot and label the point.

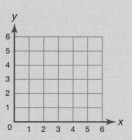

The origin is at (___**0**___, ___**0**___).

The x-coordinate is _____, so move _____ unit to the right.

The y-coordinate is _____, so move _____ units up.

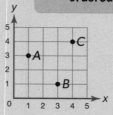
x comes before y in the alphabet, and the x-coordinate comes before the y-coordinate in an ordered pair.

B You can use an ordered pair to name a point on the coordinate plane.

DO Name the point located at (3, 1) on the coordinate plane.

1 Start at the origin.

2 The x-coordinate tells how many units to move to the right.

3 The y-coordinate tells how many units to move up.

4 Name the point.

The origin is at (_____, _____).

The x-coordinate is ____**3**____, so move _____ units to the right.

The y-coordinate is _____, so move _____ unit up.

Point _____ is located at (3, 1).

DISCUSS Gabriella says the point (2, 4) is 4 units to the right and 2 units up from the origin. Is she correct? What can you tell Gabriella?

PRACTICE

Plot and label the ordered pair on the coordinate plane.

1 (2, 5)

2 (6, 3)

Use the coordinate plane below for problems 3–6. Name the point.

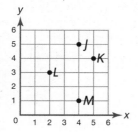

3 Point _____ is located at (4, 1).

4 Point _____ is located at (5, 4).

5 Point _____ is located at (2, 3).

6 Point _____ is located at (4, 5).

You can use ordered pairs to show relationships between two numerical patterns.

The table shows two patterns.

Rule: Add 1	Rule: Add 2
0	0
1	2
2	4
3	6
4	8

Write the pairs of values as ordered pairs.

Rule: Add 1	Rule: Add 2	Ordered Pairs
0	0	(0, 0)
1	2	(1, 2)
2	4	(2, 4)
3	6	(3, 6)
4	8	(4, 8)

You can graph the ordered pairs on a coordinate plane.

For each unit you move to the right, you move twice as many units up.

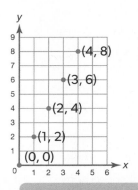

The terms in the table form pairs of values.

The terms of the first pattern are the x-coordinates, and the terms of the second pattern are the y-coordinates.

I see! Each term in the second pattern is 2 times the corresponding term in the first pattern.

DISCUSS How would the graph change if the rule of the second pattern were to add 3?

LESSON LINK

PLUG IN | **POWER UP** | **GO!**

You can follow a rule to create a pattern.

The first term is 0.

The rule is *add 2*.

0, 2, 4, 6, 8

An ordered pair is used to name a point on a coordinate plane.

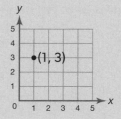

I get it! I can use two patterns to make ordered pairs. Then I can graph the ordered pairs to show the relationship between the patterns.

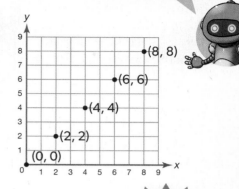

Ordered pairs are in the form (x, y).

WORK TOGETHER

Use Grid Paper to graph the numerical pattern.

- Use the terms in the table to create ordered pairs.

- Graph each ordered pair on the coordinate plane.

- Each term in the second pattern is 1 times the corresponding term in the first pattern. Each point on the graph moves to the right and up 2 units from the previous point.

Rule: Add 2	Rule: Add 2	Ordered Pairs
0	0	(0, 0)
2	2	(2, 2)
4	4	(4, 4)
6	6	(6, 6)
8	8	(8, 8)

A You can use a table to help you graph and label ordered pairs.

DO Complete the pattern in the table. Graph the pattern.

1 Write the terms in each pattern.

2 Use the terms to create ordered pairs.

3 Graph and label the ordered pairs.

4 Describe the pattern.

Rule: Add 1	Rule: Add 3	Ordered Pairs
0	0	(0, 0)
		(,)
		(,)
		(,)
		(,)

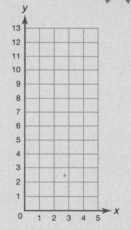

Grid Paper can be found on p. 211.

Each term in the second pattern is _____ times the corresponding term in the first pattern.

Each point on the graph moves _____ unit to the right and _____ units up from the previous point.

DISCUSS Look at these ordered pairs: (0, 0), (1, 4), (2, 8), (3, 12), (4, 16). What is the relationship between the ordered pairs?

Look at how the x- and y-coordinates change from one ordered pair to the next.

PRACTICE

Use the patterns to create ordered pairs.

1

Rule: Add 3	Rule: Add 6	Ordered Pairs
0	0	(,)
3	6	(,)
6	12	(,)
9	18	(,)
12	24	(,)

2

Rule: Add 1	Rule: Add 5	Ordered Pairs
0	0	(**0**, **0**)
1	5	(**1**, **5**)
2	10	(,)
3	15	(,)
4	20	(,)

REMEMBER
Look at the first pattern for the *x*-coordinates.

Complete each pattern and create ordered pairs. Then describe the ordered pairs of the patterns.

3

Rule: Add 1	Rule: Add 4	Ordered Pairs
0	0	(,)
		(,)
		(,)
		(,)
		(,)

_____

_____

4

Rule: Add 2	Rule: Add 6	Ordered Pairs
0	0	(**0**, **0**)
2	6	(**2**, **6**)
		(,)
		(,)
		(,)

HINT
Look at the second pattern for the *y*-coordinates.

_____

_____

5

Rule: Add 3	Rule: Add 3	Ordered Pairs
0	0	(,)
		(,)
		(,)
		(,)
		(,)

_____

_____

6

Rule: Add 4	Rule: Add 8	Ordered Pairs
0	0	(,)
		(,)
		(,)
		(,)
		(,)

_____

_____

Complete each pattern and create ordered pairs. Then graph and label the ordered pairs.

7

Rule: Add 2	Rule: Add 4	Ordered Pairs
0	0	(,)
		(,)
		(,)
		(,)
		(,)

What do you notice about the points on the graph?

_____

_____

_____

_____

Solve.

8 Thomas plotted the points (0, 0), (1, 6), (2, 12), (3, 18), and (4, 24) on a coordinate plane. What do you notice about the ordered pairs?

_____

_____

Look at how each ordered pair relates to the next ordered pair.

9 Avery used the rule *add 3* to create one pattern, and the rule *add 6* to create another pattern. Then she wrote ordered pairs. What is the relationship between the corresponding terms?

_____

_____

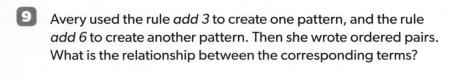

Find the Pattern

Mato used terms from two patterns to write these ordered pairs: (0, 0), (2, 8), (4, 16), (6, 24), (8, 32). Lillian says the next ordered pair will be (16, 34). What can you tell Lillian?

What were the rules for Mato's patterns?

Compare the ordered pairs to find each pattern.

PROBLEM SOLVING

NUMBER GAMES

READ

Abby uses the rule *add 5* to make a pattern. Jayden uses the rule *add 10* to make a pattern. If both girls start at 0, which number would Jayden say when Abby says 40?

Abby's Pattern Rule: Add 5	Jayden's Pattern Rule: Add 10
0	0
5	10
10	20
15	30
20	40

PLAN

• What is the problem asking you to find?

Which _____ Jayden would say when Abby says 40

• What do you need to know to solve the problem?

What is the rule for Abby's pattern? _____

What is the rule for Jayden's pattern? _____

The number that Abby says _____

• How can you solve the problem?

You can identify the relationship between the corresponding terms of the two patterns.

SOLVE

Look for a relationship between the terms of the two patterns.

$0 \times$ _____ $= 0$

$5 \times$ _____ $= 10$

$10 \times$ _____ $=$ _____

$15 \times$ _____ $=$ _____

$20 \times$ _____ $=$ _____

I get it! If I am correct, the terms of the two patterns will match my answer.

The terms in Jayden's pattern are _____ times the terms in Abby's pattern.

When Abby says 40, Jayden says $40 \times$ _____ $=$ _____.

CHECK

Find the next 4 terms for each pattern.

Abby: 0, 5, 10, 15, 20, _____, _____, _____, _____

Jayden: 0, 10, 20, 30, 40, _____, _____, _____, _____

Jayden will say _____ when Abby says 40.

PRACTICE

Use the problem-solving steps to help you.

I will look for a relationship between the terms of the two patterns.

1 Jenna writes this pattern: 0, 10, 20, 30, 40. Bailey writes this pattern: 0, 100, 200, 300, 400. If the girls continue their patterns, what number will Bailey write when Jenna writes 90?

CHECKLIST
- [ ] READ
- [ ] PLAN
- [ ] SOLVE
- [ ] CHECK

2 Robert uses the rule *add 5* to create a pattern. Kento uses the rule *add 15* to create a pattern. Both patterns start at 0. What number will Kento say when Robert says 25?

CHECKLIST
- [ ] READ
- [ ] PLAN
- [ ] SOLVE
- [ ] CHECK

3 Kyle and Jake each use a pattern to decide how many pages to read each night. Kyle's rule is to add 3 pages each night. Jake's rule is to add 6 pages each night. If Kyle reads 9 pages in a night, how many pages will Jake read?

CHECKLIST
- [ ] READ
- [ ] PLAN
- [ ] SOLVE
- [ ] CHECK

Powers of Ten

PLUG IN Understanding Place Value

Each digit in a number has a unique **place value**. The positions of the digits are important. The value of each place is 10 times the value of the place to the right.

A zero in a number is a place-holder digit. The 0 in 260 means 0 ones are part of the number.

Thousands	Hundreds	Tens	Ones
		2	6
	2	6	0
2	6	0	0

← $26 \times 10 = 260$
← $260 \times 10 = 2600$

The value of each place is $\frac{1}{10}$ the value of the place to the left.

Thousands	Hundreds	Tens	Ones
		1	8
	1	8	0
1	8	0	0

← $180 \times \frac{1}{10} = 18$
← $1,800 \times \frac{1}{10} = 180$

 Words to Know

place value
the value of a digit based on its position in a number

DISCUSS Oliver says that 45 is the same as 450, because the 0 has no value. What would you tell Oliver?

A You can use place value to compare values of numbers.

DO Compare the values of the numbers 400 and 4,000.

❶ Write the numbers in a place-value chart.

❷ Look at the positions of the digits in each number.

❸ Use multiplication to compare the values.

Thousands	Hundreds	Tens	Ones
	4	0	0
4	0	0	0

The 4 in 400 is in the ____hundreds____ place.

The 4 in 4,000 is in the _____ place.

$400 \times$ _____ $= 4,000$

Multiply by _____ to change the value of 400 to 4,000.

Look at the place value of the digit 2 in each number.

B You can use place value to compare values of numbers.

DO Compare the values of the numbers 20 and 200.

1 Write the numbers in a place-value chart.

2 Look at the positions of the digits in each number.

3 Use multiplication to compare the values.

Thousands	Hundreds	Tens	Ones
		2	0
	2	0	0

The 2 in 20 is in the _____tens_____ place.

The 2 in 200 is in the _____ place.

$200 \times$ _____ $= 20$

Multiply by _____ to change the value of 200 to 20.

PRACTICE

Compare the values of the numbers. Complete the sentence.

1

Thousands	Hundreds	Tens	Ones
		3	1
	3	1	0

Multiply by _____ to change the value of 31 to 310.

2

Thousands	Hundreds	Tens	Ones
	5	2	0
5	2	0	0

Multiply by _____ to change the value of 5,200 to 520.

Complete the sentence.

3 Multiply by _____ to change the value of 70 to 700.

4 Multiply by _____ to change the value of 39 to 390.

5 Multiply by _____ to change the value of 900 to 90.

6 Multiply by _____ to change the value of 6,500 to 650.

Multiplying One-Digit Whole Numbers by Multiples of 10

You can use place value to multiply by **multiples of 10**.

Multiply: 4×30

Think: $30 = 3$ tens

4×3 tens $= 12$ tens

$4 \times 30 = 120$

The **product** is 120.

You can use place value to multiply by multiples of 100.

Multiply: 4×300

Think: $300 = 3$ hundreds

4×3 hundreds $= 12$ hundreds

$4 \times 300 = 1,200$

The product is 1,200.

You can use place value to multiply by multiples of 1,000.

Multiply: $4 \times 3,000$

Think: $3,000 = 3$ thousands

4×3 thousands $= 12$ thousands

$4 \times 3,000 = 12,000$

The product is 12,000.

I can use the multiplication fact $4 \times 3 = 12$.

300 is also a multiple of 10 because $10 \times 30 = 300$.

I see a pattern! 12,000 is 10 times 1,200. 1,200 is 10 times 120.

 Words to Know

multiple of 10
a product of 10 and another number
$2 \times 10 = 20$
20 is a multiple of 10.

product
the result of multiplying two or more numbers
$8 \times 100 = 800$
↑
product

 DISCUSS How would you multiply 5×20?

A You can use a multiplication fact to multiply by a multiple of 10.

DO Multiply: 2×40

❶ Find a related multiplication fact.

❷ Use place value to rewrite the multiplication sentence.

❸ Write the product.

Use the multiplication fact: $2 \times \underline{\quad 4 \quad} = \underline{\quad\quad}$.

$2 \times \underline{\quad\quad}$ tens $= \underline{\quad\quad}$ tens

$2 \times 40 = \underline{\quad\quad}$

> Look for a multiplication fact to help you find the product.

B You can use a multiplication fact to multiply by a multiple of 100.

DO   Multiply: 3 × 500

1. Find a related multiplication fact.

   Use the multiplication fact: 3 × ___**5**___ = _____.

   3 × _____ hundreds = _____ hundreds

2. Use place value to rewrite the multiplication sentence.

   3 × 500 = _____

3. Write the product.

C You can use a multiplication fact to multiply by a multiple of 1,000.

DO   Multiply: 6 × 7,000

1. Find a related multiplication fact.

   Use the multiplication fact: 6 × ___**7**___ = _____.

   6 × _____ thousands = _____ thousands

2. Use place value to rewrite the multiplication sentence.

   6 × 7,000 = _____

3. Write the product.

DISCUSS Zachary said that the product of 9 × 9,000 is 81 hundreds, or 8,100. What would you tell Zachary?

PRACTICE

Use place value and a related multiplication fact to rewrite the problem. Then find the product.

1 3 × 30

Use the multiplication fact: ___**3**___ × ___**3**___ = _____.

3 × _____ tens = _____ tens

3 × 30 = _____

2 6 × 800

Use the multiplication fact: _____ × _____ = _____.

6 × _____ hundreds = _____ hundreds

6 × 800 = _____

3 2 × 7,000

Use the multiplication fact: _____ × _____ = _____.

2 × _____ _____ = _____ _____

2 × 7,000 = _____

A **power of 10** is the result of multiplying 10 by itself a certain number of times. The **exponent** in a power of 10 tells you how many times to use 10 as a factor.

Evaluate 10^3.

The exponent 3 means use the **base number**, 10, as a factor 3 times.

$10^3 = 10 \times 10 \times 10 = 1,000$

> In a power of 10, the base number is always 10.

When you multiply a number by a power of 10, the exponent tells how many places to move the **decimal point** of the number to the right.

$25 \times 10^3 = 25 \times 1000 = 25000.$

> The product shows the decimal point in 25 moved three places to the right.

When you divide by a power of 10, the exponent tells you how many places to move the decimal point of the number to the left.

$25 \div 10^3 = 25 \div 1000 = 0.025$

> The quotient shows that the decimal point in 25 moved three places to the left.

Words to Know	**decimal point (.)** a symbol that separates the whole number from the fractional part	**base number** a number that is multiplied by itself a certain number of times	**exponent** a number that tells how many times the base number is used as a factor	**power of 10** a number that is the result of multiplying 10 by itself a certain number of times

DISCUSS   How would you divide $127 \div 10$?

LESSON LINK

PLUG IN	POWER UP	GO!
You can use place value to understand the values of the digits in numbers. 4 40 ← 4 × 10 = 40 400 ← 40 × 10 = 400	You can use multiplication facts to multiply by multiples of 10. 3 × 5,000 3 × 5 = 15 3 × 5 thousands = 15 thousands 3 × 5,000 = 15,000	*I get it! I can use place value and multiplication facts to multiply and divide by powers of 10.*

WORK TOGETHER

You can move the decimal point of a number when you multiply by a power of 10.

Multiply: 36×10^2

$10^2 = 10 \times 10 = 100$

$36 \times 10^2 = 36 \times 100 = 3600$.

- First evaluate 10^2.
- Multiply by moving the decimal point in 36 two places to the right.

$36 \times 10^2 = 3,600$

A You can multiply by a power of 10.

DO Multiply: 7×10^3

1. Evaluate the power of 10.
2. Multiply by moving the decimal point in 7.
3. Write the product.

$10^3 = 10 \times 10 \times 10 = $ _____

$7 \times 10^3 = 7 \times 1000 = 7$ _____

The product shows the decimal point in 7 moved _____ places to the right.

$7 \times 10^3 = $ _____

B You can divide by a power of 10.

DO Divide: $23 \div 10^3$

1. Evaluate the power of 10.
2. Divide by moving the decimal point in 23.
3. Write the quotient.

$10^3 = 10 \times 10 \times 10 = $ _____

$23 \div 10^3 = 23 \div 1000 = 0.23$

The quotient shows the decimal point in 23 moved _____ places to the left.

$23 \div 10^3 = $ _____

DISCUSS How would you use the exponent to multiply 18×10^4?

I know the answer will be greater than 18 because multiplying by a power of 10 moves the decimal point to the right.

PRACTICE

Multiply or divide.

1 $8 \cdot 10^1$

_____

2 $12 \cdot 10^2$

_____

3 72×10

_____

4 9×10^3

$10^3 = 10 \times 10 \times 10$

$= $ _____

_____

> **HINT:**
> The power of ten tells you the place value of the answer.

5 $26 \div 10^1$

_____

6 $629 \div 10^1$

_____

7 $561 \div 10^2$

_____

8 $14 \div 10^3$

The decimal point moves ___**3**___ places to the _____.

_____

> **REMEMBER:**
> Use zeros as placeholders.

9 1.7×10^1

_____

10 $23.4 \div 10^2$

_____

Answer each question.

11 Think about the product of 4×10^4. How many places to the right does the decimal point in 4 move?

_____

12 Think about the quotient of $29 \div 10^3$. How many places to the left does the decimal point in 29 move?

_____

Solve.

13 98×10^3

_____

> The decimal point moved 3 places to the left.

14 Cindy divided 98 by a power of 10. The quotient was 0.098. By what power of 10 did Cindy divide?

_____

DISCUSS **Use the Pattern**

Ben wants to divide 138 by 10^2.

He knows that $10^2 = 100$.

How can he find the quotient?

> The exponent of the power of 10 tells me how many places to move the decimal point.

What is the quotient?

PROBLEM SOLVING

NUMBER DETECTIVE

READ

Alex multiplied 41 by a power of ten. She got the product 41,000. By what power of ten did Alex multiply?

PLAN

• What is the problem asking you to find?

The missing _____ in a multiplication problem

• What do you need to know to solve the problem?

You need to know the place value of the _____.

The product is _____.

• How can you solve the problem?

Find a power of ten that moves the decimal point in 41 to the right.

SOLVE

Find the missing factor that is a power of 10.

$41 \times ? = 41,000$

In the product 41,000, the decimal point in 41

moved _____ places to the right.

The number of places the decimal point moves is shown by the exponent of the power of 10.

So, the power of 10 is _____.

> Compare the location of the decimal point in 41 and in your answer. How many places does the decimal point move?

CHECK

Multiply your answer by 41.

Write the missing factor with an exponent: $41 \times$ _____

Write the missing factor as a whole number: $41 \times$ _____

The product is _____.

Alex multiplied 41 by _____ to get 41,000.

PRACTICE

Write a number sentence to represent the problem.

Write your answer with an exponent. Use the problem-solving steps to help you.

1 Colleen multiplied 3 by a power of 10. She got the product 300. By what power of ten did Colleen multiply?

CHECKLIST
- [ ] READ
- [ ] PLAN
- [ ] SOLVE
- [ ] CHECK

2 Pablo divided 58 by a power of 10. He got the quotient 5.8. By what power of ten did Pablo divide?

CHECKLIST
- [ ] READ
- [ ] PLAN
- [ ] SOLVE
- [ ] CHECK

3 Yusef multiplied 65 by a power of 10. He got the product 65,000. By what power of ten did Yusef multiply?

CHECKLIST
- [ ] READ
- [ ] PLAN
- [ ] SOLVE
- [ ] CHECK

4 Pavithra divided 42 by a power of 10. She got the quotient 0.042. By what power of ten did Pavithra divide?

CHECKLIST
- [ ] READ
- [ ] PLAN
- [ ] SOLVE
- [ ] CHECK

Reading and Writing Decimals

PLUG IN — Reading and Writing Whole Numbers

Thousands Period			Ones Period		
Hundreds	**Tens**	**Ones**	**Hundreds**	**Tens**	**Ones**
6	9	1	0	5	7

Place value is used to write numbers. A place-value chart separates numbers into periods.

The chart can help you read the number. Read the number in each period, and then the name of the period.

The **expanded form** for 691,057 is 600,000 + 90, 000 + 1,000 + 50 + 7.

I see! This chart shows the thousands and ones periods.

This number name is six hundred ninety-one thousand, fifty-seven.

Since there is a zero in the hundreds place, I don't write it as an addend.

expanded form

a way of writing a number that shows the sum of the values of each digit

406,285 in expanded form is 400,000 + 6,000 + 200 + 80 + 5.

DISCUSS The expanded form for 183,024 is 100,000 + 80,000 + 3,000 + 20 + 4. Why are there only 5 addends if there are 6 digits in the number?

A You can use a number name to write a number in a place-value chart.

DO Write the number two hundred ten thousand, nine hundred seventy-six.

❶ Start with the thousands period. Write each digit in its place value.

❷ Write the digits in the ones period.

Thousands Period			Ones Period		
Hundreds	**Tens**	**Ones**	**Hundreds**	**Tens**	**Ones**
2					

B You can write a number in expanded form.

DO Write 650,789 in expanded form.

> When there is a zero in the number, do not include that value in expanded form!

1 Write the value of each digit from greatest to least.

2 Separate each value with a plus sign.

The value of the digit 6 is ___**600,000**___.

The value of the digit 5 is _____.

The value of the digit 0 is _____.

The value of the digit 7 is _____.

The value of the digit 8 is _____.

The value of the digit 9 is _____.

The expanded form is

_____ + _____ + _____ + _____ + _____.

PRACTICE

Write the number name for the number. Then write the number in expanded form.

1

Thousands Period			Ones Period		
Hundreds	**Tens**	**Ones**	**Hundreds**	**Tens**	**Ones**
3	0	9	9	2	7

number name: ___**three hundred**_____

expanded form: _____ + _____ + _____ + _____ + _____

2

Thousands Period			Ones Period		
Hundreds	**Tens**	**Ones**	**Hundreds**	**Tens**	**Ones**
1	2	3	6	5	4

number name: _____

expanded form: _____ + _____ + _____ + _____ + _____ + _____

Place Value

Hundred Thousands	Ten Thousands	Thousands	Hundreds	Tens	Ones
7	4	4	5	5	1

The value of a digit depends on its place in the number.

The 4 in the ten thousands place has a value of 40,000.

The 4 in the thousands place has a value of 4,000.

$$4,000 \times 10 = 40,000$$

40,000 is **10 times** 4,000.

The 5 in the hundreds place has a value of 500.

The 5 in the tens place has a value of 50.

$$500 \div 10 = 50$$

50 is **one tenth** of 500.

I see! The value of each place is 10 times the value of the place to its right.

That makes sense! The value of each place is $\frac{1}{10}$, or a tenth, of the value of the place to its left.

Words to Know

tenth
one of ten equal parts; $\frac{1}{10}$

 DISCUSS In 444,000, what is the value of the first 4? What would its value be in relation to the 4 in the ten thousands place?

A You can use a place-value chart to compare the values of digits in a number.

DO Compare the values of the digits 6 in the number.

1 Find the value of each digit.

2 Use multiplication to compare the values.

Hundred Thousands	Ten Thousands	Thousands	Hundreds	Tens	Ones
5	1	6	6	2	3

The digit 6 in the thousands place has a value of ___**6,000**___.

The digit 6 in the hundreds place has a value of _____.

Multiply by _____ to change the value of 600 to 6,000.

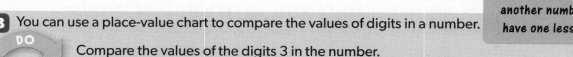

A number that is $\frac{1}{10}$ of another number will have one less zero.

B You can use a place-value chart to compare the values of digits in a number.

DO Compare the values of the digits 3 in the number.

1 Find the value of each digit.

2 Use multiplication to compare the values.

Hundred Thousands	Ten Thousands	Thousands	Hundreds	Tens	Ones
8	3	3	4	4	1

The digit 3 in the ten thousands place has a value of __**30,000**__.

The digit 3 in the thousands place has a value of _____.

Multiply by _____ to change the value of 30,000 to 3,000.

 DISCUSS How can you compare the values of the digits 4?

PRACTICE

Compare the values of the digits in the number.

1

Hundred Thousands	Ten Thousands	Thousands	Hundreds	Tens	Ones
9	9	4	8	5	7

The digit 9 in the hundred thousands place has a value of __**900,000**__.

The digit 9 in the ten thousands place has a value of _____.

Multiply by _____ to change the value of 90,000 to 900,000.

2

Hundred Thousands	Ten Thousands	Thousands	Hundreds	Tens	Ones
6	6	9	8	0	2

The digit 6 in the ten thousands place has a value of _____.

The digit 6 in the hundred thousands place has a value of _____.

Multiply by _____ to change the value of 600,000 to 60,000.

Tens	Ones	Decimal Point	Tenths	Hundredths	Thousandths
4	5	.	6	3	2

A place-value chart can help you write the number name for a **decimal**, or write it in expanded form.

To write the number name, write the whole-number part, write the decimal point as the word "and," then write the decimal part. Write the place of the last decimal digit.

Another way to write a number in expanded form is to use multiplication and place value.

4 tens = 4×10

5 ones = 5×1

6 tenths = $6 \times \frac{1}{10}$

3 **hundredths** = $3 \times \frac{1}{100}$

2 **thousandths** = $2 \times \frac{1}{1,000}$

Decimals can be written in the same ways as whole numbers.

The number name is forty-five and six hundred thirty-two thousandths.

The expanded form is $(4 \times 10) + (5 \times 1) + \left(6 \times \frac{1}{10}\right) + \left(3 \times \frac{1}{100}\right) + \left(2 \times \frac{1}{1,000}\right)$.

Words to Know

decimal
a number with a decimal value to the right of a decimal point

hundredth
one of one hundred equal parts; $\frac{1}{100}$

thousandth
one of one thousand equal parts; $\frac{1}{1,000}$

DISCUSS Look at the place values of each digit to the right of the decimal point in the place-value chart above. How would you write each decimal place as a fraction?

LESSON LINK

PLUG IN	POWER UP	GO!

Place value is used to read and write whole numbers.

The number name for 720,911 is seven hundred twenty thousand, nine hundred eleven.

The value of the digit depends on its place value.

In 720,911, the 1 in the tens place represents 10, and the 1 in the ones place represents 1.

I see! I can use what I know about place value of whole numbers to help me read and write decimals.

WORK TOGETHER

You can use Decimal Place-Value Chart to write the number name of a decimal.

- The whole-number part is *eighty-one.*

- Write "and" for the decimal point.

- The decimal part is *four hundred seventy-six.*

- The place value of the last digit is *thousandths.*

Write the number name for the decimal 81.476.

Tens	Ones	Decimal Point	Tenths	Hundredths	Thousandths
8	1	.	4	7	6

The number name is "eighty-one and four hundred seventy-six thousandths."

> **Decimal Place-Value Chart** can be found on p. 215.

A You can use a Place-Value Chart to find the value of each digit.

DO Write twenty-nine and four hundred thirty-five thousandths in expanded form.

1. Use the number name to write the decimal in the chart.

2. Find the value of each digit in the decimal.

3. Write the value of each digit using multiplication.

4. Write the sum of the values in expanded form using plus signs.

Tens	Ones	Decimal Point	Tenths	Hundredths	Thousandths

$2 \text{ tens} = 20 = 2 \times 10$

$9 \text{ ones} = 9 = 9 \times$ ____

$4 \underline{\hspace{2cm}} = \dfrac{\square}{\square} = \underline{\hspace{0.5cm}} \times \dfrac{\square}{\square}$

$3 \underline{\hspace{2cm}} = \dfrac{\square}{\square} = \underline{\hspace{0.5cm}} \times \dfrac{\square}{\square}$

$5 \underline{\hspace{2cm}} = \dfrac{\square}{\square} = \underline{\hspace{0.5cm}} \times \dfrac{\square}{\square}$

$(\underline{\hspace{0.7cm}} \times 10) + (\underline{\hspace{0.7cm}} \times 1) + \left(\underline{\hspace{0.7cm}} \times \frac{1}{10}\right) + \left(\underline{\hspace{0.7cm}} \times \frac{1}{100}\right) +$

$\left(\underline{\hspace{0.7cm}} \times \frac{1}{1,000}\right)$

DISCUSS Marco wrote the number 51.934 as $(5 \times 10) + (1 \times 1) + (9 \times 10) + (3 \times 100) + (4 \times 1,000)$. What can you tell Marco about his work?

> I can find the sum of the addends in Marco's number in expanded form and see if it is equal to the decimal.

PRACTICE

Write the number name for each decimal.

Decimal Place-Value Chart can be found on p. 217.

1 18.428

The whole-number part is ___eighteen___.

The decimal part is _____.

The place value of the last digit is _____.

The number name is _____ and _____ thousandths.

REMEMBER
The word "and" stands for the decimal point.

2 79.86

The whole-number part is ___seventy-nine___.

The decimal part is _____.

The place value of the last digit is _____.

The number name is _____.

HINT
Use the place value of the last decimal digit to write the last word in the decimal's name.

3 67.217

The number name is _____.

4 401.33

The number name is _____.

5 52.099

The number name is _____.

6 11.603

The number name is _____.

Write each decimal in expanded form. If needed, use a Place-Value Chart.

7 35.789

(_____ × 10) + (_____ × 1) + (_____ × $\frac{1}{10}$) + (_____ × $\frac{1}{100}$) + (_____ × $\frac{1}{1,000}$)

8 47.18

(_____ × _____) + (_____ × _____) + (_____ × $\frac{\square}{\square}$) + (_____ × $\frac{\square}{\square}$)

9 12.467

_____

10 68.102

_____

Write the decimal.

11 Frieda writes the number name thirty-nine and one hundred sixteen thousandths. What is the decimal? _____

12 Victor writes a decimal in expanded form:
(9 × 10) + (8 × 1) + (6 × $\frac{1}{10}$) + (4 × $\frac{1}{100}$) + (5 × $\frac{1}{1,000}$). What is the decimal? _____

I know! I have to use place value to write the number shown.

The last word of the number name describes the place of the last digit on the right of a decimal number.

DISCUSS **Justify Your Answer**

Quinn and Joan want to use numbers to write the decimal "four and eight hundred five thousandths." Quinn says they should write 4.85. Joan disagrees.

Is Quinn or Joan correct?

How do you know?

PROBLEM SOLVING

WRITING A CHECK

DOLLARS

READ

Irene is writing a check to pay for a car repair. The cost is $172.43. How does she write the number name for the amount?

PLAN

• What is the problem asking you to find?

Write the _____ for $172.43.

• What do you need to know to solve this problem?

The _____ of each digit

• How can you solve the problem?

The money amount $172.43 is a _____, so I can use a place-value chart to write the number name.

SOLVE

Write the decimal in the place-value chart.

Hundreds	Tens	Ones	Decimal Point	Tenths	Hundredths

Use the chart to write the number name.

The whole-number part is _____.

The decimal part is _____.

What is another way to say one hundredth of a dollar? _____

Rewrite the decimal part in cents. _____

The number name is _____ dollars

and _____ cents.

CHECK

Look at the number name you wrote. Write the amount shown by your number name.

$_____

Your amount should be the same as the amount of Irene's car repair.

Irene writes the number name for the amount of her car repair as

_____.

PRACTICE

I can write the decimal in a place-value chart.

Use the problem-solving steps to help you.

1 Two cities are 628.47 miles apart. Beth says the distance is $(6 \times 100) + (2 \times 10) + (8 \times 1) + \left(4 \times \frac{1}{10}\right) + \left(7 \times \frac{1}{100}\right)$ in expanded form. Jason says that it is $(6 \times 10) + (2 \times 1) + \left(8 \times \frac{1}{10}\right) + \left(4 \times \frac{1}{100}\right) + \left(7 \times \frac{1}{1,000}\right)$. Who is correct? How do you know?

CHECKLIST
- [ ] READ
- [ ] PLAN
- [ ] SOLVE
- [ ] CHECK

2 Sean biked four hundred sixty-two and seventy-one hundredths miles in one month. Write the expanded form for this decimal.

CHECKLIST
- [ ] READ
- [ ] PLAN
- [ ] SOLVE
- [ ] CHECK

3 Charlotte wants to show the value of each digit in the decimal 87.321. Should she write the number name or the expanded form? Write the decimal both ways. Circle the way that most clearly shows the value of each digit.

CHECKLIST
- [ ] READ
- [ ] PLAN
- [ ] SOLVE
- [ ] CHECK

4 Comparing Decimals

PLUG IN Comparing Whole Numbers

Thousands	Hundreds	Tens	Ones
4	3	8	9
4	3	7	2

You can use place value to help you compare numbers. Compare the digits from left to right.

The digits in the thousands and hundreds places are the same. The digits in the tens place are different.

Compare the values of the tens digits.

Use > **(greater than)**, = **(equal to)**, or < **(less than)**.

$$4,389 > 4,372$$

80 is greater than 70, so **4,389** is greater than **4,372**.

Words to Know

greater than (>) a symbol that shows that the first quantity is more than the second quantity	equal to (=) a symbol that shows that two quantities have the same value	less than (<) a symbol that shows that the first quantity is less than the second quantity

---

DISCUSS

Eli earned $120 mowing lawns. Reid earned $120 babysitting. Using place value, explain how you know they both earned the same amount of money.

A You can use a place-value chart to compare numbers.

DO Compare 13,272 and 13,541.

❶ Write the numbers in a place-value chart.

Ten Thousands	Thousands	Hundreds	Tens	Ones
1	3	2	7	2

❷ Compare the values of the digits in the first place where they are different.

200 is _____ than 500, so 13,272 is _____ than 13,541.

❸ Write <, =, or >.

13,272 ◯ 13,541

B You can line up numbers by place value to compare them.

> *I get it! The 8 and the 3 are in the ones place of these numbers.*

DO   Compare 4,278 and 4,253.

1 Write the first number you are comparing.

2 Write 4,253 below 4,278. Line up the digits in the ones place.

3 Compare the values of the digits in each place from left to right.

4 Write >, =, or <.

4 , 2   7   8

| 4 | | | |

The digits in the _____ place and _____ place are the same.

The first place in which the digits are different is in the _____ place.

70 is _____ than 50, so 4,278 is _____ than 4,253.

4,278 ◯ 4,253

PRACTICE

Write the numbers in the place-value chart. Write >, =, or < to compare the numbers.

1   9,245 ◯ 9,248

Ten Thousands	Thousands	Hundreds	Tens	Ones
	9	2	4	5

2   37,469 ◯ 36,582

Ten Thousands	Thousands	Hundreds	Tens	Ones

Write >, =, or < to compare the numbers.

3   7,564 ◯ 7,710

4   85,324 ◯ 85,196

5   13,704 ◯ 30,417

6   29,005 ◯ 8,698

Writing Decimals

Hundreds	Tens	Ones	Decimal Point	Tenths	Hundredths	Thousandths
	4	3	.	8	9	

To write the number name of the decimal, write the digits to the left of the decimal point as a whole number: "forty-three"

Write the digits to the right of the decimal point as a whole number: "eighty-nine"

Use the place value of the last decimal digit to name the decimal part of the number.

The number name is "forty-three and eighty-nine hundredths."

> I see! I need to write "and" to stand for the decimal point.

To write the decimal in expanded form, begin at the greatest place value and write the value of each digit as a multiplication expression.

$$4 \text{ tens} = 4 \times 10$$
$$3 \text{ ones} = 3 \times 1$$
$$8 \text{ tenths} = 8 \times \frac{1}{10}$$
$$9 \text{ hundredths} = 9 \times \frac{1}{100}$$
$$(4 \times 10) + (3 \times 1) + \left(8 \times \frac{1}{10}\right) + \left(9 \times \frac{1}{100}\right)$$

> I get it! The expanded form lists the sum of the values of each digit in the decimal.

DISCUSS In the place-value chart above, why is the thousandths place left blank? Could you write a decimal equal to the decimal above with a digit in the thousandths place?

A You can use a place-value chart to write the number name of a decimal.

DO Write the number name of 2.413.

1. Write the decimal in the chart.

2. Read the digit to the left of the decimal point. Write the number name.

3. Write "*and*" for the decimal point.

4. Read the digits to the right of the decimal point. Write the number name.

5. Use the place value of the last digit to name the decimal part.

Ones	Decimal Point	Tenths	Hundredths	Thousandths
2	.	4	1	3

The number name of the digit to the left of the decimal point is _____.

The number name of the digits to the right of the decimal point is _____.

The number name is _____

_____.

B You can use place value to write a decimal in expanded form.

DO Write 6.837 in expanded form.

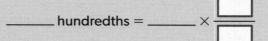

I can write the decimal in a place-value chart to help me find the value of each digit.

1 Write the value of each digit as a multiplication expression.

$6 \text{ ones} = 6 \times 1$

$8 \text{ tenths} = 8 \times \dfrac{\boxed{1}}{\boxed{10}}$

2 Write the expanded form of the decimal.

_____ hundredths = _____ $\times \dfrac{\boxed{}}{\boxed{}}$

_____ thousandths = _____ $\times \dfrac{\boxed{}}{\boxed{}}$

$6.837 = (6 \times 1) + \left(8 \times \dfrac{1}{10}\right) + \left(3 \times \dfrac{\boxed{}}{\boxed{}}\right) + \left(\underline{} \times \dfrac{\boxed{}}{\boxed{}}\right)$

DISCUSS A question on Alisha's math test asks students to write the decimal 52.709 in expanded form. Her answer is shown below.

$$52.709 = (5 \times 10) + (2 \times 1) + \left(7 \times \dfrac{1}{10}\right) + \left(9 \times \dfrac{1}{100}\right)$$

Is Alisha's answer correct? Explain why or why not.

PRACTICE

Write the number name of the decimal.

1 251.38

two hundred fifty-one _____

2 91.75

_____

Write the decimal in expanded form.

3 15.36

_____

4 68.971

_____

Decimal Place-Value Chart can be found on p. 219.

Comparing Decimals

Hundreds	Tens	Ones	Decimal Point	Tenths	Hundredths	Thousandths
	6	3	.	5	2	
	6	3	.	8	1	

Compare the digits in each place in the chart from left to right. Find the first place where the digits are different.

The tens and ones digits are the same. The tenths digits are different.

Compare the values of the digits. Then write $>$, $=$, or $<$ to compare the decimals.

The digit 5 has a value of $\frac{5}{10}$.

The digit 8 has a value of $\frac{8}{10}$.

$63.52 < 63.81$

I know! Since 5 tenths is less than 8 tenths, 63.52 is less than 63.81.

 DISCUSS

Ryan says that comparing decimals is just like comparing whole numbers. Do you agree or disagree with Ryan? Explain why.

LESSON LINK

PLUG IN

You can use place value to compare whole numbers.

$5,213 > 5,146$

$200 > 100$

POWER UP

You can use place value to write decimals in expanded form.

$3.72 = (3 \times 1) + \left(7 \times \frac{1}{10}\right) + \left(2 \times \frac{1}{100}\right)$

GO!

I get it! I can use the value of each digit to compare decimals, just as I do with whole numbers.

When the decimal points are lined up, the place values of all of the digits are lined up, too!

WORK TOGETHER

You can use place value to compare two decimals.

- Write the decimals so that the decimal points are lined up.

- The ones digits are the same. The tenths digits are the same.

- The hundredths digits are different. Compare the values of the digits.

9.628 is less than 9.643.

Compare 9.628 and 9.643.

9.628

9.643

The digit 2 represents $\frac{2}{100}$.

The digit 4 represents $\frac{4}{100}$.

2 hundredths is less than 4 hundredths.

So, 9.628   9.643.

A You can use a place-value chart to compare the decimals.

DO   Compare 4.682 and 4.391. Use >, =, or <.

1. Write the decimals in a place-value chart.

2. Compare the digits in each place from left to right.

3. Compare the values of the digits in the first place where they are different.

4. Compare the decimals using >, =, or <.

Ones	Decimal Point	Tenths	Hundredths	Thousandths

The first place in which the digits are different is the _____ place.

The digit 6 represents ▭/▭ .

The digit 3 represents ▭/▭ .

6 tenths is _____ than 3 tenths.

4.682 ◯ 4.391

Compare digits of numbers from left to right.

DISCUSS   Hanna says that 42.153 is less than 41.478 because $\frac{3}{1,000}$ is less than $\frac{8}{1,000}$.
What would you say to Hanna?

PRACTICE

Use a place-value chart to compare the decimals. Write >, =, or <.

1 316.9 ◯ 316.5

Hundreds	Tens	Ones	Decimal Point	Tenths	Hundredths	Thousandths
3	1	6	.	9		
3	1	6	.	5		

2 29.547 ◯ 29.528

Hundreds	Tens	Ones	Decimal Point	Tenths	Hundredths	Thousandths

3 6.034 ◯ 6.225

Hundreds	Tens	Ones	Decimal Point	Tenths	Hundredths	Thousandths

4 857.312 ◯ 856.392

Hundreds	Tens	Ones	Decimal Point	Tenths	Hundredths	Thousandths

Write >, =, or < to compare. Use a place-value chart if needed.

5 76.201 ◯ 76.187

6 5.084 ◯ 5.084

> **Decimal Place-Value Chart** can be found on p. 221.

7 17.86 ◯ 17.68

8 495.216 ◯ 495.261

> I know! I can compare the decimals, one place value at a time.

Solve.

9 Megan picked 18.342 pounds of apples. Jason picked 18.407 pounds of apples. Whose apples weighed more? _____

10 During the storm, 1.226 inches of rain fell in Evansville and 1.262 inches of rain fell in Springdale. Which town received more rain? _____

DISCUSS   **See the Relationship**

Darius is comparing the decimals 52.687 and 52.493.

He knows that 52.687 > 52.493.

How can he compare the decimals using a "less than" symbol (<)?

> The < symbol points to the lesser number.

Compare the decimals. _____ < _____

PROBLEM SOLVING

MEASURING UP

READ A factory makes electrical wire. A wire must be less than 1.255 millimeters in diameter to be accepted. Will a wire with a diameter of 1.249 millimeters be accepted?

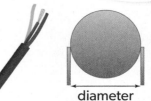

diameter

PLAN
- What is the problem asking you to find?

    Whether or not a wire with a diameter of _____ millimeters will be accepted

- What do you need to know to solve the problem?

    Is 1.249 greater than or less than _____?

- How can you solve the problem?

    Compare _____ and _____.

SOLVE Line up the decimals by their decimal points.

1	.	2	4	9

> When I compare decimals, I need to find the first place value where the digits are different.

The first place in which the digits are different is the _____ place.

4 hundredths is _____ than 5 hundredths.

Compare: 1.249 ◯ 1.255

CHECK Use a place-value chart.

Ones	Decimal Point	Tenths	Hundredths	Thousandths

The wire _____ be accepted.

I can line up the decimals by their decimal points to compare, or I can write them in a place-value chart.

PRACTICE

Compare the decimals using >, =, or <. Use the problem-solving steps to help you.

1 A truck can carry a maximum load of 2.566 tons. A company needs to ship 2.665 tons of furniture. Tell whether the truck will be able to carry the furniture.

CHECKLIST
- [ ] READ
- [ ] PLAN
- [ ] SOLVE
- [ ] CHECK

2 To qualify for a track meet, Carmen needs to finish the 100-meter sprint in less than 12.29 seconds. At practice, she ran the sprint in 12.26 seconds. Tell whether Carmen qualifies for the track meet.

CHECKLIST
- [ ] READ
- [ ] PLAN
- [ ] SOLVE
- [ ] CHECK

3 Shawn is packing a lamp in a box. The box is 53.97 centimeters high. The lamp is 54.01 centimeters high. Tell whether the lamp will fit into the box.

CHECKLIST
- [ ] READ
- [ ] PLAN
- [ ] SOLVE
- [ ] CHECK

Multiplying Whole Numbers

PLUG IN Multiplying by Multiples of 10

Place-value models can help you multiply by a multiple of 10.

Multiply: 3×70

Show 3 groups of 70.
Then make groups of 100.

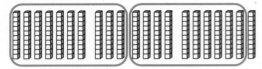

After regrouping, count the models to find the **product**.

$$3 \times 70 = 210$$

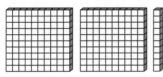

I regroup 20 tens as 2 hundreds and add 1 ten to get 210.

You can also find the product of 3×70 using multiplication facts.

Think of a multiplication fact that has 3 and 7 as **factors**.

$$3 \times 7 = 21$$

Use this fact to multiply by the multiple of 10.

$$3 \times \mathbf{70} = 21\mathbf{0}$$

I see a pattern! As the factor increases by a multiple of 10, so does the product.

Words to Know

product	factor
the result of multiplying two or more numbers	a number that is multiplied to set a product

 DISCUSS

Why could you use both 3×4 and 4×3 to multiply 3×40?

A You can use place-value models to multiply by a multiple of 10.

 DO

Multiply: 4×60

1 Show 4 groups of 60.

2 Regroup 10 tens as 1 hundred. Regroup again, as needed.

3 Count the models to find the product.

_____1_____ hundred + _____ hundred + _____ tens = _____

$4 \times 60 =$ _____

B You can use multiplication facts to multiply by multiples of 10.

I can think of 6 × 30 as 6 × 3 tens, which is equal to 18 tens or 180!

DO Multiply: 6 × 30

❶ Think of a multiplication fact that has 6 and 3 as factors.

❷ Multiply the factors.

❸ Write the product.

Multiplication fact: ___6___ × _____

_____ × _____ = _____

6 × 30 = _____

PRACTICE

Use place-value models to find the product.

1 6 × 60 = __360__

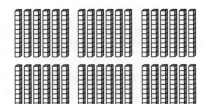

2 5 × 80 = _____

3 3 × 90 = _____

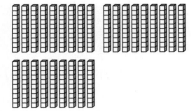

4 7 × 50 = _____

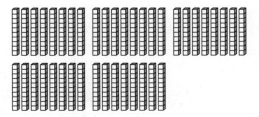

Use a multiplication fact to find the product.

5 3 × 30 = _____

Multiplication fact:

_____ × _____ = _____

6 5 × 60 = _____

Multiplication fact:

_____ × _____ = _____

7 8 × 70 = _____

Multiplication fact:

_____ × _____ = _____

8 9 × 40 = _____

Multiplication fact:

_____ × _____ = _____

Multiplying by 1- and 2-Digit Factors

You can use an **area model** to help multiply whole numbers.

Multiply: 13×16

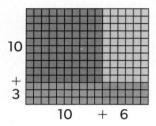

Write an equation for each section of the model.

$$10 \times 10 = 100$$
$$10 \times 3 = 30$$
$$6 \times 10 = 60$$
$$6 \times 3 = 18$$

Add the products: $100 + 30 + 60 + 18 = 208$
The product of 13×16 is 208.

> I can write factors as a sum of tens and ones to help me draw my model.

You can multiply whole numbers using place value.

Multiply: 13×16

Set up the problem vertically. Line up the digits with the same place value.

$$
\begin{array}{r}
1\!\!\!/ \\
16 \\
\times 13 \\
\hline
148 \quad \leftarrow 16 \times 3 \\
+160 \quad \leftarrow 16 \times 10 \\
\hline
208
\end{array}
$$

> I add the two partial products to find the total product of 208!

Words to Know

area model
a model that shows the size of a surface in square units

 DISCUSS

William used an area model to multiply 14×5. Wendy used an area model to multiply 5×14. Will their products be the same? Explain.

A You can use an area model to find a product.

 DO

Multiply: 7×16

1 Write 16 as the sum of tens and ones.

2 Shade the model.

3 Write the equation for each section of the model.

4 Add the partial products.

5 Write the total product.

$16 = \underline{\quad 10 \quad} + \underline{\qquad}$

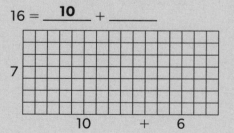

$10 \times 7 = \underline{\qquad}$ $6 \times 7 = \underline{\qquad}$

$\underline{\qquad} + \underline{\qquad} = \underline{\qquad}$

$7 \times 16 = \underline{\qquad}$

B You can use place value to find a product.

DO Multiply: 43 × 25

1 Line up the digits with the same place value.

2 Multiply 43 by 5 ones.

3 Multiply 43 by 2 tens.

4 Add the partial products.

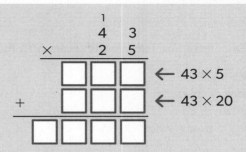

← 43 × 5

← 43 × 20

43 × 25 = _____

DISCUSS

Brynn draws an area model to find the product of 14 × 12. She found partial products and the total product. What can you tell Brynn about her work?

$7 \times 6 = 42 \qquad 7 \times 6 = 42$
$7 \times 6 = 42 \qquad 7 \times 6 = 42$
$42 + 42 + 42 + 42 = 168$

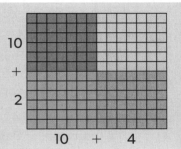

PRACTICE

Use an area model to find the product.

1 11 × 3 = _____

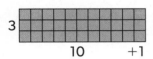

10 × _____ = _____

3 × _____ = _____

_____ + _____ = _____

2 12 × 7 = _____

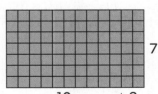

10 × _____ = _____

2 × _____ = _____

_____ + _____ = _____

Multiply.

3
```
  3 1
× 1 7
```

4
```
  1 2
× 1 4
```

5
```
  6 3
× 2 8
```

Multiply 2,417 × 4.

Set up the problem vertically. Line up the digits with the same place value.

Multiply the **ones** by 4.
    4 × 7 ones = 28 ones
    Regroup the ones.
    28 ones = 2 tens 8 ones

$$\begin{array}{r} \overset{1\;\;2}{2\,4\,1\,7} \\ \times\quad\quad 4 \\ \hline 9\,6\,6\,8 \end{array}$$

Multiply the **tens** by 4.
    4 × 1 ten = 4 tens
    Add the regrouped tens.
    4 tens + 2 tens = 6 tens

Multiply the **hundreds** by 4.
    4 × 4 hundreds = 16 hundreds
    Regroup the hundreds.
    16 hundreds = 1 thousand 6 hundreds

I always multiply the ones first.

I see! I need to regroup when the product of the digits is a 2-digit number.

Multiply the **thousands** by 4.
    4 × 2 thousands = 8 thousands
    Add the regrouped thousands.
    8 thousands + 1 thousand = 9 thousands

2,417 × 4 = 9,668

 DISCUSS How is setting up the problem vertically to multiply similar to finding a product using partial products and place value?

LESSON LINK

PLUG IN	POWER UP	GO!
You can use place-value models and multiplication facts to multiply by multiples of 10.	You can multiply two factors with and without area models.	I can use what I know about multiples of 10, place value, and multiplying vertically to multiply numbers with 3 or more digits!

$$7 \times 6 = 42$$
$$7 \times 60 = 420$$

$$\begin{array}{r} \overset{2}{1\,4} \\ \times\,1\,5 \\ \hline 1\,7\,0 \\ +1\,4\,0 \\ \hline 2\,1\,0 \end{array}$$

I need to cross out the regrouping when I move to the next step.

WORK TOGETHER

You can use the standard algorithm to multiply whole numbers.

• Write the problem vertically.

• Think of 14 as 1 ten and 4 ones. Multiply 236 by 4 ones. Regroup when necessary.

• Multiply 236 by 1 ten, or 10.

• Add the partial products to find the total product.

$236 \times 14 = 3{,}304$

Multiply: 236×14

```
      ₁ ₂
    2 3 6
  ×   1 4
    9 4 4
+ 2 3 6 0
  3 3 0 4
```

A You can set up a problem vertically to multiply.

DO Multiply: $2{,}352 \times 9$

❶ Multiply the ones. Regroup.

❷ Multiply the tens. Add the regrouped tens. Regroup.

❸ Multiply the hundreds. Add the regrouped hundreds. Regroup.

❹ Multiply the thousands. Add the regrouped thousands.

```
  2 3 5 2
×       9
```

$2{,}352 \times 9 = $ _____

B You can use place value to multiply.

DO Multiply: 118×38

❶ Think of 38 as 3 tens and 8 ones. Multiply 118 by 8 ones.

❷ Multiply 118 by 3 tens. Remember that this partial product will have zero in the ones place.

❸ Add the partial products.

❹ Write the product.

```
    1 1 8
×    3 8
```

$118 \times 38 = $ _____

 DISCUSS

Tyler solves $21{,}719 \times 3$ in this way. What can you tell Tyler about his work?

```
  2 1,7 1 9
×        3
  6 5,1 3 7
```

Solve the problem without first looking at Tyler's work. Then compare your answer to Tyler's.

PRACTICE

Multiply.

1
```
      6
  3 1 0 9
 ×      7
  ─────────
      6 3
```

REMEMBER
Remember to add the regrouped tens.

2
```
  4 3 2 2
 ×      2
```

3
```
  1 9 7 8
 ×      6
```

4
```
  5 7 3 4
 ×      3
```

HINT
The second partial product will have 0 in the ones place because you are multiplying by a multiple of 10.

5
```
    1 3 7
 ×   4 1
```

6
```
    1 2 6
 ×   1 2
```

7
```
    1 7 5
 ×   3 5
```

8
```
    9 1 3
 ×   2 2
```

Multiply.

9
$$\begin{array}{r} 1457 \\ \times \quad 5 \\ \hline \end{array}$$

10
$$\begin{array}{r} 8282 \\ \times \quad 8 \\ \hline \end{array}$$

11
$$\begin{array}{r} 475 \\ \times \quad 64 \\ \hline \end{array}$$

12
$$\begin{array}{r} 213 \\ \times \quad 93 \\ \hline \end{array}$$

Solve.

13 A machine puts 6 eggs in a carton. If there are 7,812 cartons, how many eggs will be needed to fill them all? _____

> Remember to write the problem vertically and line up the place values!

14 Jonas is planting evergreen trees. He plants 114 rows with 36 trees in each row. How many evergreen trees will Jonas plant? _____

> Compare the total number of hamburger buns purchased this year with the number of hamburgers sold last year.

DISCUSS

Use Reasoning

For the fall fair, a school buys 45 cases of hamburger buns. There are 48 buns in a case. Last year, 2,049 hamburgers were sold. If the planners predict they will sell about the same amount of hamburgers this year, have enough buns been purchased?

Will the school have enough hamburger buns? How do you know?

PROBLEM SOLVING

MAKING PROGRAMS

READ Ms. Reed is making programs for a band concert. Each program contains 14 sheets of paper. If she makes 250 programs, how many sheets of paper will she need in all?

PLAN
- What is the problem asking you to find?

    The total _____ that Ms. Reed needs

- What do you need to know to solve the problem?

    There are _____ programs and _____ sheets of paper in a program.

- How can you find the total number of sheets of paper?

    Multiply the number of _____ by the number

    of _____.

SOLVE Multiply.

Write 250 × 14 vertically.

Multiply 250 by 4 ones. Regroup when necessary.

Multiply 250 by 1 ten.

Add the partial products.

250 × 14 = _____

CHECK Use place value to check.

14 is the same as 1 ten and 4 ones. You can multiply 250 × 10 and 250 × 4, and then add the partial products.

250 × 10 = _____

250 × 4 = _____

Add the partial products.

_____ + _____ = _____

Ms. Reed needs _____ sheets of paper in all.

Line up the place values, and remember to regroup when necessary.

PRACTICE

Use the problem-solving steps to help you.

1 Marisol bought 12 strings of lights to decorate the trees in her yard. Each string has 125 lights. How many lights did Marisol buy?

CHECKLIST
- [ ] READ
- [ ] PLAN
- [ ] SOLVE
- [ ] CHECK

2 At the factory, 24 pencils are packed in each box. There are 175 boxes in one case. How many pencils are in each case?

CHECKLIST
- [ ] READ
- [ ] PLAN
- [ ] SOLVE
- [ ] CHECK

3 A carton of golf tees contains 1,427 tees. How many tees are in 8 cartons?

CHECKLIST
- [ ] READ
- [ ] PLAN
- [ ] SOLVE
- [ ] CHECK

Dividing Whole Numbers

PLUG IN — Dividing by 1-Digit Divisors

Divide: 474 ÷ 3

1 Set up the problem vertically. 474 is the **dividend** and 3 is the **divisor**.

2 Divide the 4 hundreds by 3. Write 1 in the hundreds place of the **quotient**. Subtract 3.

3 Bring down 7 tens. Divide 17 tens by 3. Write 5 in the tens place of the quotient. Subtract 15.

4 Bring down 4 ones. Divide 24 ones by 3. Write 8 in the ones place of the quotient. Subtract 24. The quotient is 158.

5 Use a model to check the answer. 158 = 100 + 50 + 8. Multiply 3 by each of the **partial quotients**. The sum of those products is 474.

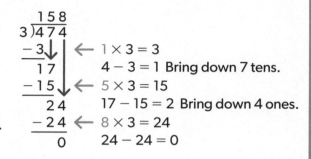

$$
\begin{array}{r}
158 \\
3\overline{)474} \\
-3 \leftarrow 1 \times 3 = 3 \\
\hline
17 \quad 4 - 3 = 1 \text{ Bring down 7 tens.} \\
-15 \leftarrow 5 \times 3 = 15 \\
\hline
24 \quad 17 - 15 = 2 \text{ Bring down 4 ones.} \\
-24 \leftarrow 8 \times 3 = 24 \\
\hline
0 \quad 24 - 24 = 0
\end{array}
$$

100	50	8
$\begin{array}{r}100\\ \times\ 3\\ \hline 300\end{array}$	$\begin{array}{r}50\\ \times\ 3\\ \hline 150\end{array}$	$\begin{array}{r}8\\ \times\ 3\\ \hline 24\end{array}$

3

This model shows 300 + 150 + 24 or 474.

> I see! I can use place value and multiplication to divide whole numbers.

Words to Know	**dividend** the number to be divided $\begin{array}{r}70\\ 6\overline{)420}\end{array}$ ← dividend	**divisor** the number by which the dividend is divided divisor → $6\overline{)\begin{array}{r}70\\ 420\end{array}}$	**quotient** the answer in a division problem $\begin{array}{r}70\\ 6\overline{)420}\end{array}$ ← quotient	**partial quotient** the value of part of a quotient, or the value of one digit in a quotient In 272 ÷ 8 = 34, 30 and 4 are partial quotients.

DISCUSS Why can you use a model to check your answer for a division problem?

Divide from left to right.

A You can use multiplication and place value to divide.

DO Divide: 294 ÷ 6

❶ Set up the problem vertically.

❷ Divide 29 tens by 6. The first digit of the quotient will be in the tens place.

❸ Bring down 4 ones. Divide the ones by 6.

❹ Use a model to check your answer.

4☐

6)2 9 4

← 4 × 6 = ___

29 − 24 = __

← 9 × __ = ___

___ − ___ = __

6

PRACTICE

Divide. Use the area model to check.

❶

1☐☐

4)7 4 0

← 4 × 1 = **4**

7 − 4 = __

← 4 × __ = ___

___ − ___ = __

← 4 × __ = ___

___ − ___ = __

4

The quotient is _____.

Divide.

❷ 5)645

❸ 3)201

❹ 9)2142

The quotient is _____.

The quotient is _____.

The quotient is _____.

You can find the **product** of two multi-digit numbers by breaking apart one **factor** into its place-value parts.

Multiply: 238 × 14

Think of 14 as 1 ten and 4 ones. Multiply the ones and then the tens. Add the **partial products**.

$$
\begin{array}{r}
238 \\
\times\ \ 14 \\
\hline
952 \\
+\ 2380 \\
\hline
3332
\end{array}
$$

← 238 × 4 ones
← 238 × 1 ten

> I get it! First I multiply 238 by 4 ones. Then I multiply 238 by 1 ten.

You can multiply a four-digit number by a two-digit number using the same method.

Multiply: 3,719 × 25

$$
\begin{array}{r}
3719 \\
\times\ \ 25 \\
\hline
18595 \\
+\ 74380 \\
\hline
92975
\end{array}
$$

← 3719 × 5 ones
← 3719 × 2 tens

> I can think of 25 as 2 tens and 5 ones.

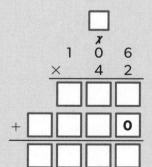

Words to Know

product	factor	partial product
the answer in a multiplication problem	a number that is multiplied to get a product	the result of multiplying one part of one factor by a second factor

DISCUSS Which factor would you break into place-value parts if you were going to multiply 2,468 × 79? Why?

A You can use place value to multiply.

DO Multiply: 106 × 42

1. Align the numbers using place value.

2. Find the partial product for the ones. Multiply 106 × 2 ones. Regroup as needed.

3. Find the partial product for the tens. Multiply 106 × 4 tens. Regroup as needed.

4. Add the partial products to find the total product.

$$
\begin{array}{r}
1\ 0\ 6 \\
\times\ \ 4\ 2 \\
\hline
\square\ \square\ \square \\
+\ \square\ \square\ \square\ 0 \\
\hline
\square\ \square\ \square\ \square
\end{array}
$$

106 × 42 = _____

> I see! The partial product for the tens wil always be a multiple of 10 and have a zero in the ones place.

Write a 0 in the partial product for the tens.

B You can find partial products to multiply.

DO Multiply: 4,621 × 37

1. Write the greater factor above the lesser factor and align them by place value.

2. Find the partial product for the ones. Multiply 4,621 × 7 ones. Regroup as needed.

3. Find the partial product for the tens. Multiply 4,621 × 3 tens. Regroup as needed.

4. Add the partial products to find the total product.

```
      □
    □ □
    4 6 2 1
×       3 7
  □ □ □ □ □
+ □ □ □ □ □
  □ □ □ □ □ □
```

4,621 × 37 = _____

DISCUSS Nari multiplied 120 × 13 and got 480, as shown. What error did he make?

```
    1 2 0
×     1 3
    3 6 0
+   1 2 0
    4 8 0
```

PRACTICE

Multiply.

1
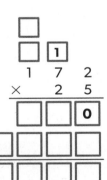
```
      □
    □ 1
  1 7 2
×   2 5
  □ □ □ 0
+ □ □ □ □
  □ □ □ □
```

2
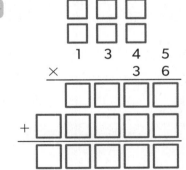
```
    □ □ □
    □ □ □
  1 3 4 5
×     3 6
  □ □ □ □
+ □ □ □ □
  □ □ □ □ □
```

3
```
    4 5 8
×    1 9
```

4
```
    7 2 5
×    3 3
```

Dividing Whole Numbers

Divide: 1,609 ÷ 12

1. **Divide hundreds.** Divide 16 hundreds by 12. Write 1 in the hundreds place of the quotient. Subtract 12.

2. **Divide tens.** Bring down 0 tens. Divide 40 tens by 12. Write 3 in the tens place of the quotient. Subtract 36.

3. **Divide ones.** Bring down 9 ones. Divide 49 ones by 12. Write 4 in the ones place of the quotient. Subtract 48. There are no more digits to bring down, so 1 is the **remainder**. The quotient is 134 R1. (R indicates the remainder.)

4. **Draw a model to check your answer.** 134 = 100 + 30 + 4. Multiply 12 by each of those values. Then add the remainder, 1. If your quotient is correct, the sum will be 1,609.

```
        1 3 4  R1
  12)1 6 0 9
     - 1 2 ↓        ← 1 × 12 = 12
         4 0          16 − 12 = 4  Bring down 0 tens.
       - 3 6 ↓      ← 3 × 12 = 36
           4 9        40 − 36 = 4  Bring down 9 ones.
         - 4 8      ← 4 × 12 = 48
             1        49 − 48 = 1  The remainder is 1.
```

	100	30	4
12	100 × 12 = 1200	30 × 12 = 360	4 × 12 = 48

This model shows 12 × 134 = 1,200 + 360 + 48 = 1,608.

The remainder, 1, is added: 1,608 + 1 = 1,609. ✓

> I see! When I check my answer, I multiply the divisor by the whole-number part of the quotient and then add the remainder.

Words to Know

remainder
the number that is left over after division is complete

DISCUSS How do you know if there is a remainder when you divide?

LESSON LINK

PLUG IN

You can multiply and use place value to divide.

```
        5 8
   2)1 1 6
    - 1 0 ↓     ← 5 × 2 = 10
       1 6        11 − 10 = 1
     - 1 6      ← 8 × 2 = 16
         0        16 − 16 = 0
```

POWER UP

You can multiply by finding partial products, and adding them.

```
        1
      3 3
    1 0 4 5
  ×     2 7
    7 3 1 5    ← 1045 × 7 ones
+ 2 0 9 0 0    ← 1045 × 2 tens
  2 8 2 1 5
```

GO!

> I get it! I can use place value and the relationship between multiplication and division to divide multi-digit numbers.

I get it! Using a model is one way to use multiplication to check my answer. This is another way!

WORK TOGETHER

You can use standard algorithm to divide whole numbers.

Divide: 810 ÷ 19

- Divide 81 tens by 19.

- Bring down 0 ones. Divide 50 ones by 19. Subtract 38.

- There are no more digits to bring down, so 12 is the remainder.

- Use multiplication to check the answer.

810 ÷ 19 = 42 R12

```
        4 2  R12
  19 ) 8 1 0
      − 7 6 ↓   ← 4 × 19 = 76
        5 0       81 − 76 = 5
      − 3 8     ← 2 × 19 = 38
        1 2       50 − 38 = 12 (remainder)
```

```
     3
     1
     1 9
   ×   4 2
      3 8   ← 19 × 2 ones
   + 7 6 0  ← 19 × 4 tens
    7 9 8
```

Add the remainder:
798 + 12 = 810 ✓

A You can multiply and use place value to divide.

DO Divide: 4,294 ÷ 34

1 Divide 42 hundreds by 34.

2 Bring down 9 tens. Divide the tens by 34.

3 Bring down 4 ones. Divide the ones by 34.

4 Use multiplication to check your answer.

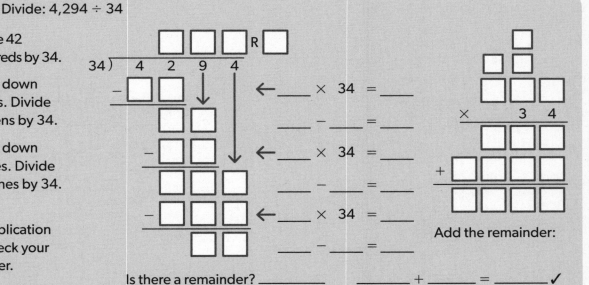

Is there a remainder? _____

4,294 ÷ 34 = _____

_____ + _____ = _____ ✓

Add the remainder:

DISCUSS Sam's answer to 625 ÷ 12 was 52 R1. He used multiplication to check and determined that his answer was incorrect because the product was not 625. What can you tell Sam about his work?

```
      5 2 1
    ×   1 2
    1 0 4 2
  + 5 2 1 0
    6 2 5 2
```

PRACTICE

Divide. Use multiplication or a model to check your answer. Show your work.

1

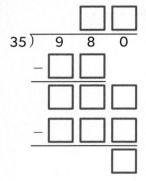

```
        □ □
35 ) 9  8  0
   − □ □
     □ □ □
   − □ □ □
         □
```

2

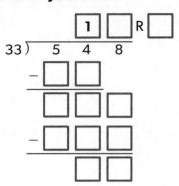

```
         1 □ R □
33 ) 5  4  8
   − □ □
     □ □ □
   − □ □ □
       □ □
```

3

```
        □ □ □
19 ) 2  3  3  7
   − □ □
     □ □
   − □ □
       □ □
     − □ □
         □
```

4

```
         □ □ R □
52 ) 1  2  5  0
   − □ □ □
     □ □ □
   − □ □ □
         □
```

Divide. Show your work.

5 300 ÷ 25 = _____

6 714 ÷ 34 = _____

7 928 ÷ 46 = _____

8 2,488 ÷ 71 = _____

9 4,838 ÷ 41 = _____

10 3,900 ÷ 72 = _____

Use division to solve.

11 Mrs. Weitzman has 528 stickers. She divides them equally among her 22 students. How many stickers does each student get?

_____

12 The baking club baked 208 muffins for a school breakfast. Each tin held 16 muffins. How many tins were there?

_____

I am going to multiply and use place value to divide.

DISCUSS

Reason about Another's Work

Anita divided 672 ÷ 26 and got 24 R48 as her answer. Juan says he knows that Anita's answer cannot be correct. Explain how Juan could know this without seeing Anita's work.

Compare the divisor to the remainder.

PROBLEM SOLVING

OUTSIDE THE BOX

READ

There are 2,790 cans of food collected for the food bank.
The cans are placed in boxes that hold 24 cans each.
How many boxes will be filled? How many cans will be left over?

PLAN

• What is the problem asking you to find?

   The number of full boxes and the number of _____

• What do you need to know to solve the problem?

   There are _____ cans. Each box holds _____ cans.

SOLVE

Set up and solve the division problem.

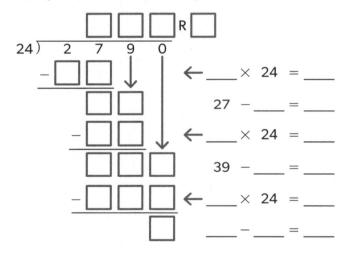

24) 2 7 9 0

← ____ × 24 = ____

27 − ____ = ____

← ____ × 24 = ____

39 − ____ = ____

← ____ × 24 = ____

____ − ____ = ____

CHECK

Use multiplication to check your answer.

Add the product and the remainder to check.

_____ + _____ = _____

_____ boxes will be filled. _____ cans will be left over.

> Remember that the remainder cannot be greater than the divisor.

PRACTICE

Use the problem-solving steps to help you.

1 The 220 participants in a charity walk line up in rows for a newspaper photo. There are 15 people in each row. Any walkers not in rows will kneel in front of the first row. How many full rows are there? How many people are kneeling?

CHECKLIST
- [ ] READ
- [ ] PLAN
- [ ] SOLVE
- [ ] CHECK

2 A group of volunteers planted 1,440 tulip bulbs in the park. They planted 36 rows of bulbs, with the same number of bulbs in each row. How many bulbs in each row did they plant?

CHECKLIST
- [ ] READ
- [ ] PLAN
- [ ] SOLVE
- [ ] CHECK

3 There are 1,050 athletes and coaches going to a professional baseball game. Each bus holds 55 people. Only full buses will be rented for the trip. Any extra people will take cars. How many buses will be rented? How many people will take cars?

CHECKLIST
- [ ] READ
- [ ] PLAN
- [ ] SOLVE
- [ ] CHECK

Dividing Decimals

PLUG IN Adding and Subtracting Decimals

Add: 1.4 + 1.2

Use models to add **decimals**.

Model 1.4 and 1.2. Add the wholes that are completely shaded. Then add the shaded tenths.

There are 2 wholes and 6 tenths shaded.

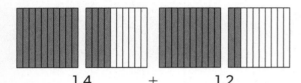

1.4   +   1.2

1.4 + 1.2 = 2.6

This place-value chart has a place for a **decimal point**.

	Ones	Decimal Point	Tenths	Hundredths
	1		1	
	1	.	6	8
+	1	.	3	4
	3	.	0	2

As with whole numbers, I may need to regroup when I add decimals.

Subtract: 2.25 − 1.12

Use models to subtract decimals.

Model 2.25. Cross out 1 whole and 12 shaded hundredths. The difference will be the number of shaded squares left.

There is 1 whole and 13 hundredths left.

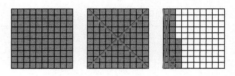

2.25 − 1.12 = 1.13

Place value can also be used to subtract.

	Ones	Decimal Point	Tenths
	2 / 3	.	14 / 4
−	1	.	9
	1	.	5

I need to put the decimal point in my answer.

Words to Know

decimal
a number with a decimal point

decimal point (.)
a symbol that separates the whole number from the fractional part

DISCUSS How is adding and subtracting decimals like adding and subtracting whole numbers? How is it different?

A You can use a model to add and subtract decimals.

DO Add: 1.7 + 1.1

❶ Shade the models.

❷ Add the number of whole shaded models.

❸ Add the number of shaded tenths.

❹ Write the sum.

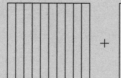 +

___1.7___   _____

1.7 + 1.1 = _____

B You can use place value to add and subtract decimals.

DO Subtract: 3.52 − 2.61

❶ Write each number in the place-value chart.

❷ Subtract the decimals. Regroup when necessary.

❸ Write the difference.

	Ones	Decimal Point	Tenths	Hundredths
	3	.	5	2

PRACTICE

Shade the model to show addition. Write the sum.

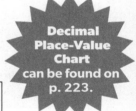
Decimal Place-Value Chart can be found on p. 223.

1 2.3 + 1.6 = _____

  +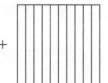

Shade the model and then cross out the part being subtracted. Write the difference.

2 4.7 − 2.6 = _____

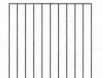 

Add or subtract. You may draw models or use a place-value chart to help you.

3 6.5 + 1.8 = _____

4 4.16 + 3.09 = _____

5 5.4 − 2.9 = _____

6 3.32 − 1.71 = _____

POWER UP | Multiplying Decimals

Multiply: 2×1.4

Use models to multiply a whole number by a decimal.

Show 2 groups of 1 whole and 4 tenths.

There are 2 wholes and 8 tenths shaded.

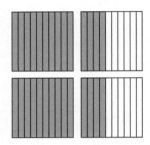

$$2 \times 1.4 = 2.8$$

Write the problem vertically.

$$
\begin{array}{r}
1\,.\,4 \leftarrow \text{1 decimal place} \\
\times \quad 2 \leftarrow \text{0 decimal places} \\
\hline
2\,.\,8 \leftarrow \text{1 decimal place}
\end{array}
$$

> I show 2 models of 1.4 because I'm multiplying the whole number, 2, by the decimal 1.4.

Multiply: 0.6×0.2

Use models to multiply a decimal by a decimal.

Shade 0.6 on the first model. Shade 0.2 on the second model. Combine the models. The overlapping part, 12 hundredths, is the product.

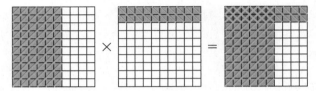

$$0.6 \times 0.2 = 0.12$$

Write the problem vertically. Multiply decimals as if they were whole numbers. Then find the number of decimal places in the product.

$$
\begin{array}{r}
0\,.\,6 \leftarrow \text{1 decimal place} \\
\times 0\,.\,2 \leftarrow \text{1 decimal place} \\
\hline
0\,.\,12 \leftarrow 1 + 1 = \text{2 decimal places}
\end{array}
$$

> Remember to write the decimal point in the product.

DISCUSS How many decimal places will there be in the product of 3×2.4? Explain how you know.

A You can use a model to multiply a whole number by a decimal.

DO Multiply: 3×1.7

1. Shade each pair of models to show 1.7.

2. Count the number of shaded wholes and tenths. Regroup.

3. Write the product.

    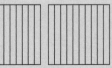 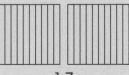

1.7   1.7   1.7

$$3 \times 1.7 = \underline{\hspace{1.5cm}}$$

B You can use a model to multiply two decimals.

DO

Multiply: 0.3 × 0.8

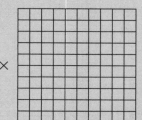
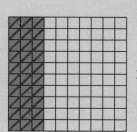
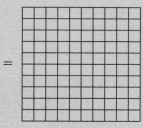

① Shade and draw a / in the first model to show 0.3.

② Shade and draw a \ in the second model to show 0.8.

③ Shade both factors on the third model. Draw an x in squares with shading in common.

④ Write the product.

The overlapping part is the product.

0.3 × 0.8 = _____

DISCUSS

Jody drew this model. What factors and product does the model show?

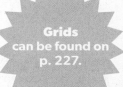

PRACTICE

Use the model to find the product.

1 2 × 2.9 = _____

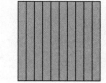

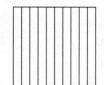

Multiply. You may draw models to help you.

2 3 × 1.5 = _____

3 0.8 × 0.7 = _____

Grids can be found on p. 227.

4 0.1 × 0.9 = _____

5 0.4 × 0.6 = _____

6 1.2 × 0.2 = _____

7 2.4 × 0.6 = _____

Dividing Decimals

Divide: 1.8 ÷ 3

Use models to divide a decimal by a whole number.

Show 1.8 with models.

Divide the 18 tenths into 3 equal groups.

There are 6 tenths, or 0.6, in each group.

$$1.8 \div 3 = 0.6$$

> I see! The whole number tells me how many equal groups to divide the decimal into.

Divide a decimal by a whole number or by another decimal.

Divide: 1.4 ÷ 2

```
   0.7
2)1.4
 -1 4  ← 7 × 2
    0  ← 14 − 14
```

Place the decimal point in the quotient.

Divide 14 tenths by 2.

That's 7 tenths, or 0.7, in each group.

$$1.4 \div 2 = 0.7$$

Divide: 3.6 ÷ 0.4

First, multiply the divisor and the dividend by 10 to make each decimal a whole number.

$$10 \times 3.6 = 36$$
$$10 \times 0.4 = 4$$

Place the decimal point in the quotient.

Divide 36 by 4.

That's 9 in each group.

```
    9.
4)36
 -36  ← 9 × 4
   0  ← 36 − 36
```

$$3.6 \div 0.4 = 9$$

> When I divide a decimal with tenths by another decimal with tenths, the quotient is a whole number.

DISCUSS Explain how you can check your answer to one of the division problems above.

LESSON LINK

PLUG IN

You can use models or place value to add and subtract decimals.

```
   1
  3.43
 +1.29
  4.72
```

POWER UP

You can use models or place value to multiply decimals.

```
    1
   2.3
 ×   4
   9.2
```

GO!

> OK! Knowing how to use place value will help me divide decimals.

WORK TOGETHER

You can use Grids to help you divide a decimal by a whole number.

- Shade the model to show 1.6 divided into 2 equal groups.

- Show the division without a model.

1.6 ÷ 2 = 0.8

Be sure to place the decimal point in the quotient.

Divide: 1.6 ÷ 2

$$\begin{array}{r} 0.8 \\ 2{\overline{)1.6}} \\ -1\,6 \\ \hline 0 \end{array}$$

There are 8 tenths, or 0.8, in each group.

Grids can be found on p. 229.

A You can use a model to divide a decimal by a whole number.

DO Divide: 1.2 ÷ 3

1. Shade the model to show 1.2 divided into 3 equal groups.

2. Show the division without a model.

3. Write the quotient.

$$3{\overline{)1.2}}$$

There are _____ tenths,

or _____, in each group.

1.2 ÷ 3 = _____

B You can divide a decimal by a decimal.

DO Divide: 2.8 ÷ 0.7

1. Multiply the divisor by 10 to make it a whole number.

2. Multiply the dividend by 10.

3. Write the division problem. Place the decimal point in the quotient. Divide.

4. Write the quotient.

10 × 0.7 = _____

10 × 2.8 = _____

2.8 ÷ 0.7 = _____

DISCUSS Rachel divided 2.1 by 0.3 and got the quotient 0.7. What can you tell Rachel about her work?

To check, multiply the quotient by the divisor and see if the product equals the dividend.

PRACTICE

Divide. Show your work. You may draw models to help you.

1 1.6 8 _____

HINT
Multiply to check
your answer.

$$8\overline{)1.6}$$

2 2.1 3 _____

Grids
can be found
on p. 231.

3 3.5 ÷ 5 = _____

4 2.4 ÷ 4 = _____

5 3.6 ÷ 0.6 = _____

10 × 0.6 = _____

10 × 3.6 = _____

REMEMBER
Multiply the divisor by
10 to make it a whole
number. Then multiply
the dividend by 10.

6 1.8 ÷ 0.9 = _____

10 × 0.9 = _____

10 × 1.8 = _____

7 2.5 ÷ 0.5 = _____

8 3.2 ÷ 0.4 = _____

Divide.

9 $7.2 \div 8 =$ _____

10 $5.6 \div 0.7 =$ _____

Solve.

11 Anna used 4.8 yards of fabric to make 6 pillows. If she used the same amount of fabric to make each pillow, how much fabric did she use for each? _____

12 Keagan used 2.8 pounds of chocolate chips to make 4 batches of cookies. If he used the same amount of chocolate chips in each batch, how many pounds of chocolate chips did he use for each? _____

> Before I divide a decimal by a whole number, I need to bring the decimal point up to the quotient.

DISCUSS

Describing Patterns

Len solved the division problems below. In each set, he noticed patterns in the quotients. Divide. Look for patterns.

$8.1 \div 0.9 =$ _____ $1.5 \div 0.3 =$ _____ $7.2 \div 0.9 =$ _____

$8.1 \div 9 =$ _____ $1.5 \div 3 =$ _____ $7.2 \div 9 =$ _____

$81 \div 9 =$ _____ $15 \div 3 =$ _____ $72 \div 9 =$ _____

$6.3 \div 0.7 =$ _____ $5.4 \div 0.9 =$ _____ $2.8 \div 0.7 =$ _____

$6.3 \div 7 =$ _____ $5.4 \div 9 =$ _____ $2.8 \div 7 =$ _____

$63 \div 7 =$ _____ $54 \div 9 =$ _____ $28 \div 7 =$ _____

Describe any patterns you see.

PROBLEM SOLVING

MEASURING PLANT GROWTH

READ Juan's plant grew 8.1 inches over a 9-week period. If the plant grew the same amount each week, how many inches did it grow each week?

PLAN • What is the problem asking you to find?

How many _____ per _____ Juan's plant grew

• What do you need to know to solve the problem?

Juan's plant grew _____ inches.

Juan measured the plant's growth over _____ weeks.

• How can you solve the problem?

You can divide the number of _____ by the number of _____.

SOLVE Divide: 8.1 ÷ 9

Show your work.

CHECK Multiply the quotient by the divisor.

Multiply 9 × _____. Show your work.

Determine the total number of decimal places in both factors, and write the decimal point in the product.

Juan's plant grew _____ inch each week.

PRACTICE

I can multiply to check my answers!

Use the problem-solving steps to help you.

1 A box of fruit snacks contains pouches that weigh 0.8 ounce each. The box weighs 6.4 ounces. How many pouches of fruit snacks are in the box?

CHECKLIST
- [ ] READ
- [ ] PLAN
- [ ] SOLVE
- [ ] CHECK

2 Brad collected 7.5 inches of rain in a jar over a period of 3 days. If it rained the same amount each day, what was the amount of rainfall per day?

CHECKLIST
- [ ] READ
- [ ] PLAN
- [ ] SOLVE
- [ ] CHECK

3 Karen used 2.4 cups of sugar to make 4 pies. If she used the same amount of sugar for each pie, how much sugar did she use for each?

CHECKLIST
- [ ] READ
- [ ] PLAN
- [ ] SOLVE
- [ ] CHECK

Adding and Subtracting Fractions with Unlike Denominators

PLUG IN Adding and Subtracting Mixed Numbers

You can use equivalent **improper fractions** to subtract **mixed numbers**.

Subtract: $3\frac{1}{3} - 1\frac{2}{3}$

① Rename each mixed number as an improper fraction. Multiply the whole number by the **denominator**. Then add the **numerator**.

$3\frac{1}{3} \rightarrow (3 \times 3) + 1 = 10 \rightarrow \frac{10}{3}$

$1\frac{2}{3} \rightarrow (1 \times 3) + 2 = 5 \rightarrow \frac{5}{3}$

② Subtract the improper fractions.

$\frac{10}{3} - \frac{5}{3} = \frac{5}{3}$

③ Rename the difference as a mixed number. Divide the numerator by the denominator.

$\frac{5}{3} = 5 \div 3 = 1\,R2$

$\frac{5}{3} = 1\frac{2}{3}$

④ Use addition to check.

$1\frac{2}{3} + 1\frac{2}{3} = \frac{5}{3} + \frac{5}{3} = \frac{10}{3} = 3\frac{1}{3}$

$3\frac{1}{3} - 1\frac{2}{3} = 1\frac{2}{3}$

> The sum is the numerator, and the denominator stays the same.

> The remainder is the numerator, and the denominator stays the same.

Words to Know

improper fraction	mixed number	denominator	numerator
a fraction in which the numerator is greater than or equal to the denominator $\frac{8}{5}$	a fraction that has a whole-number part and a fractional part $2\frac{1}{4}$	the bottom number in a fraction, which tells the total number of equal parts $\frac{1}{4} \leftarrow$ denominator	the top number in a fraction, which tells how many parts are being described numerator $\rightarrow \frac{1}{4}$

DISCUSS Deena says that $\frac{9}{9}$ is not a fraction. Is Deena correct? Explain.

A You can write mixed numbers as improper fractions to add them.

DO Add: $1\frac{1}{5} + 2\frac{2}{5}$

1 Rename each mixed number as an improper fraction.

$1\frac{1}{5} \rightarrow (1 \times 5) + 1 = \underline{\ \ 6\ \ } \rightarrow \dfrac{\boxed{}}{\boxed{5}}$

2 Add the improper fractions.

$2\frac{2}{5} \rightarrow (2 \times 5) + 2 = \underline{\hspace{2em}} \rightarrow \dfrac{\boxed{}}{\boxed{5}}$

3 Rename the sum as a mixed number.

$\dfrac{\boxed{}}{\boxed{}} + \dfrac{\boxed{}}{\boxed{}} = \dfrac{\boxed{}}{\boxed{}}$

$\underline{\hspace{3em}} \div \underline{\hspace{3em}} = \underline{\hspace{3em}} \text{R} \underline{\hspace{3em}}$

$1\frac{1}{5} + 2\frac{2}{5} = \boxed{}\,\dfrac{\boxed{}}{\boxed{}}$

B You can find equivalent improper fractions to subtract mixed numbers.

DO Subtract: $2\frac{5}{6} - 1\frac{1}{6}$

1 Rename each mixed number as an improper fraction.

$2\frac{5}{6} = \dfrac{\boxed{}}{\boxed{6}} \qquad\qquad 1\frac{1}{6} = \dfrac{\boxed{}}{\boxed{}}$

2 Subtract the improper fractions.

$\dfrac{\boxed{}}{\boxed{}} - \dfrac{\boxed{}}{\boxed{}} = \dfrac{\boxed{}}{\boxed{}}$

3 Rename the difference as a mixed number.

$\underline{\hspace{3em}} \div \underline{\hspace{3em}} = \underline{\hspace{3em}} \text{R} \underline{\hspace{3em}}$

$2\frac{5}{6} - 1\frac{1}{6} = \boxed{}\,\dfrac{\boxed{}}{\boxed{}}$

PRACTICE

Add or subtract.

1 $1\frac{2}{4} + 3\frac{1}{4} = \boxed{}\,\dfrac{\boxed{}}{\boxed{}}$

2 $3\frac{4}{5} - 2\frac{3}{5} = \boxed{}\,\dfrac{\boxed{}}{\boxed{}}$

Understanding Equivalent Fractions

You can use models to find **equivalent fractions**.

$\frac{1}{4}$	$\frac{1}{4}$	$\frac{1}{4}$	$\frac{1}{4}$

$\frac{1}{8}$	$\frac{1}{8}$	$\frac{1}{8}$	$\frac{1}{8}$	$\frac{1}{8}$	$\frac{1}{8}$	$\frac{1}{8}$	$\frac{1}{8}$

- The first model has 4 equal parts and 1 part shaded. $\frac{1}{4}$ of the model is shaded.

- The second model has 8 equal parts and 2 parts shaded. $\frac{2}{8}$ of the model is shaded.

- Compare the parts of the models. The size of each part is different, but the total shaded area is the same in both models, so the fractions are equivalent.

You can also use multiplication to find equivalent fractions.

- Multiply the numerator and denominator by the same number.

$$\frac{1}{4} = \frac{1}{4} \times \frac{2}{2} = \frac{1 \times \mathbf{2}}{4 \times \mathbf{2}} = \frac{2}{8}$$
$$\frac{1}{4} = \frac{2}{8}$$

I see! When I multiply the numerator and denominator by the same number, it's just like multiplying by 1. So, the value of the fraction doesn't change.

Words to Know

equivalent fractions
fractions that name the same value but have different numerators and denominators

$$\frac{1}{4} = \frac{2}{8} = \frac{3}{12}$$

DISCUSS Cole says the value of $\frac{1}{2}$ changes when you multiply the numerator and denominator by 4. What can you tell Cole?

A You can shade a model to show equivalent fractions.

DO Write an equivalent fraction to the fraction shown by the rectangle on the left.

1. Compare the size of the two rectangles.

2. Count the number of equal parts in each rectangle.

3. Look at the amount that is shaded in the rectangle on the left.

4. Shade the same amount in the rectangle on the right.

5. Write the equivalent fractions.

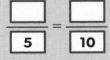

$$\frac{\Box}{5} = \frac{\Box}{10}$$

B You can use multiplication to find equivalent fractions.

Multiply both the numerator and denominator by the same number.

DO Find a fraction that is equivalent to $\frac{3}{4}$.

1 Use a fraction that equals 1, such as $\frac{3}{3}$.

2 Multiply the numerator by 3.

3 Multiply the denominator by 3.

$$\frac{3}{4} = \frac{3 \times \boxed{3}}{4 \times \boxed{}} = \frac{\boxed{}}{\boxed{}}$$

The fraction $\dfrac{\boxed{}}{\boxed{}}$ is equivalent to $\frac{3}{4}$.

DISCUSS Does the value of a fraction change when you multiply the numerator and denominator by the same number? Explain.

PRACTICE

Shade the model to show a fraction equivalent to the fraction shown. Then write the equivalent fraction.

1

$$\frac{1}{3} = \frac{\boxed{}}{\boxed{12}}$$

2

$$\frac{1}{2} = \frac{\boxed{}}{\boxed{}}$$

Multiply to find an equivalent fraction.

3 $\dfrac{2}{3} = \dfrac{2 \times \boxed{}}{3 \times \boxed{5}} = \dfrac{\boxed{}}{\boxed{15}}$

4 $\dfrac{1}{6} = \dfrac{1 \times \boxed{}}{6 \times \boxed{}} = \dfrac{\boxed{}}{\boxed{18}}$

Are the fractions equivalent? Write *yes* or *no*.

5 $\frac{1}{5}, \frac{3}{15}$

_____

6 $\frac{3}{7}, \frac{3}{9}$

_____

Adding and Subtracting Fractions with Unlike Denominators

You can use equivalent fractions to add or subtract fractions with unlike denominators.

Add: $\frac{1}{2} + \frac{1}{4}$

1 Use fraction strips to model the problem.

| $\frac{1}{2}$ | $\frac{1}{2}$ | $+$ | $\frac{1}{4}$ | $\frac{1}{4}$ | $\frac{1}{4}$ | $\frac{1}{4}$ |

2 Both addends must have the same denominator. Show $\frac{1}{2}$ as an equivalent fraction with a denominator of 4.

| $\frac{1}{4}$ | $\frac{1}{4}$ | $\frac{1}{4}$ | $\frac{1}{4}$ | $+$ | $\frac{1}{4}$ | $\frac{1}{4}$ | $\frac{1}{4}$ | $\frac{1}{4}$ |

3 Add the numerators. Write the sum over the denominator.

$$\frac{2}{4} + \frac{1}{4} = \frac{3}{4}$$

So, $\frac{1}{2} + \frac{1}{4} = \frac{3}{4}$.

You can also use equivalent fractions to add or subtract mixed numbers with unlike denominators.

Subtract: $2\frac{3}{4} - 1\frac{1}{3}$

1 Rename each mixed number as an equivalent improper fraction.

$$2\frac{3}{4} = \frac{11}{4} \qquad\qquad 1\frac{1}{3} = \frac{4}{3}$$

2 Write equivalent fractions with 12 as the common denominator.

$$\frac{11}{4} = \frac{11 \times 3}{4 \times 3} = \frac{33}{12} \qquad \frac{4}{3} = \frac{4 \times 4}{3 \times 4} = \frac{16}{12}$$

3 Subtract the numerators of the improper fractions. Use 12 as the denominator.

$$\frac{33}{12} - \frac{16}{12} = \frac{17}{12}$$

4 Rename the difference as a mixed number.

$$\frac{17}{12} = 1\frac{5}{12}$$

So, $2\frac{3}{4} - 1\frac{1}{3} = 1\frac{5}{12}$.

> I remember! Common denominator means the denominators of two different fractions are the same.

DISCUSS Why do you need to change fractions with unlike denominators to equivalent fractions before you add or subtract?

LESSON LINK

PLUG IN

You can use equivalent improper fractions to add and subtract mixed numbers with like denominators.

$$2\frac{1}{3} + 1\frac{1}{3} = \frac{7}{3} + \frac{4}{3}$$
$$= \frac{11}{3}$$
$$= 3\frac{2}{3}$$

POWER UP

You can find equivalent fractions that name the same amount.

$$\frac{1}{3} = \frac{2}{6} = \frac{3}{9}$$

GO!

> I get it! I can use equivalent fractions to add and subtract mixed numbers with unlike denominators.

When rewriting fractions, make sure you use a common denominator.

WORK TOGETHER

Use Fraction Strips to add.

Add: $\frac{2}{5} + \frac{1}{2}$

- Model the problem with fraction strips.

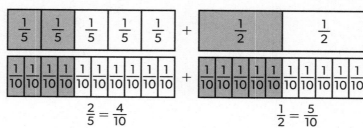

- Model each fraction as an equivalent fraction with a denominator of 10.

$$\frac{2}{5} = \frac{4}{10} \qquad \frac{1}{2} = \frac{5}{10}$$

- Add the numerators. Write the sum over the denominator.

$$\frac{4}{10} + \frac{5}{10} = \frac{9}{10}$$

So, $\frac{2}{5} + \frac{1}{2} = \frac{9}{10}$.

- Use familiar fractions to check that your answer is reasonable.

$\frac{2}{5}$ is close to but less than $\frac{1}{2}$, and $\frac{1}{2} + \frac{1}{2} = 1$, so a sum that is close to but less than 1 is reasonable.

A You can use fraction strips to model equivalent fractions.

Add: $\frac{1}{8} + \frac{3}{4}$

Fraction Strips can be found on p. 235.

❶ Model $\frac{1}{8} + \frac{3}{4}$ with fraction strips.

❷ Model $\frac{3}{4}$ as an equivalent fraction with a denominator of 8.

❸ Add the numerators. Write the sum over the denominator.

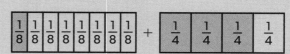

$$\frac{\boxed{}}{\boxed{}} + \frac{\boxed{}}{\boxed{}} = \frac{\boxed{}}{\boxed{}}$$

$$\frac{1}{8} + \frac{3}{4} = \frac{\boxed{}}{\boxed{}}$$

Check that your answer is reasonable.

_____

_____

 DISCUSS Ian wants to add $\frac{2}{3}$ and $\frac{1}{12}$. He says he can write equivalent fractions with a denominator of 6. What can you tell Ian?

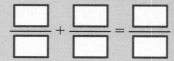 Find a denominator that you can use for both fractions.

PRACTICE

Use fraction strips to add or subtract.

1

$\frac{1}{6}$	$\frac{1}{6}$	$\frac{1}{6}$	$\frac{1}{6}$	$\frac{1}{6}$	$\frac{1}{6}$

$\frac{1}{3}$	$\frac{1}{3}$	$\frac{1}{3}$

$$\frac{1}{6} + \frac{2}{3}$$
$$\downarrow$$
$$\frac{1}{6} + \frac{4}{6} = \frac{\square}{\square}$$

2

$\frac{1}{8}$	$\frac{1}{8}$	$\frac{1}{8}$	$\frac{1}{8}$	$\frac{1}{8}$	$\frac{1}{8}$	$\frac{1}{8}$	$\frac{1}{8}$

$\frac{1}{4}$	$\frac{1}{4}$	$\frac{1}{4}$	$\frac{1}{4}$

$$\frac{7}{8} - \frac{3}{4}$$
$$\downarrow$$
$$\frac{7}{8} - \frac{\square}{8} = \frac{\square}{\square}$$

> **REMEMBER**
> Find a fraction with a denominator of 8 that is equivalent to $\frac{3}{4}$.

Add.

3 $\quad \frac{1}{5} + \frac{3}{10}$
$$\downarrow$$
$$\frac{\square}{10} + \frac{3}{10} = \frac{\square}{\square}$$

> **HINT**
> Multiply the numerator and denominator by the same number.

4 $\quad \frac{1}{4} + \frac{3}{8}$
$$\downarrow$$
$$\frac{\square}{\square} + \frac{3}{8} = \frac{\square}{\square}$$

Subtract.

5 $\quad \frac{6}{8} - \frac{1}{4}$
$$\downarrow$$
$$\frac{6}{8} - \frac{\square}{\square} = \frac{\square}{\square}$$

6 $\quad \frac{4}{5} - \frac{3}{10}$
$$\downarrow$$
$$\frac{\square}{\square} - \frac{3}{10} = \frac{\square}{\square}$$

7 $\quad \frac{9}{12} - \frac{4}{6}$
$$\downarrow$$
$$\frac{9}{12} - \frac{\square}{\square} = \frac{\square}{\square}$$

8 $\quad \frac{6}{12} - \frac{1}{3}$
$$\downarrow$$
$$\frac{6}{12} - \frac{\square}{\square} = \frac{\square}{\square}$$

Add or subtract. Rename each sum or difference as a mixed number.

9 $3\frac{3}{10} + 2\frac{2}{5} =$ ☐ $\frac{☐}{☐}$

10 $2\frac{1}{12} + 4\frac{3}{6} =$ ☐ $\frac{☐}{☐}$

11 $5\frac{1}{2} - 1\frac{1}{6} =$ ☐ $\frac{☐}{☐}$

12 $6\frac{7}{10} - 3\frac{1}{2} =$ ☐ $\frac{☐}{☐}$

Solve.

13 Carlotta ran $\frac{5}{8}$ mile on Saturday and $\frac{1}{4}$ mile on Sunday. How far did she run in all?

_____

14 Devin and Cole have to wash 12 plates. Devin has washed $\frac{5}{12}$ of the plates. Cole has washed $\frac{1}{3}$ of the plates. What fraction of the plates have the boys washed?

_____

Look for clue words to decide whether to add or subtract.

Find a common denominator before adding.

DISCUSS

Check the Reasoning

Katie is making two batches of trail mix from two different recipes. One recipe calls for $\frac{1}{2}$ cup of raisins and the other recipe calls for $\frac{1}{4}$ cup of raisins. Katie says she will need $\frac{2}{6}$ cup of raisins in all. Is Katie correct? Explain why or why not.

What quantity of raisins will Katie need in all?

PROBLEM SOLVING

HOUSE BUILDING

READ — Mrs. King is building a dollhouse. The house is $\frac{1}{2}$ yard tall and the roof is $\frac{1}{6}$ yard tall. How tall will the dollhouse be when the roof is attached?

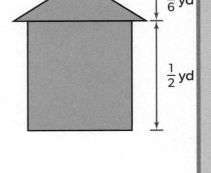

$\frac{1}{6}$ yd

$\frac{1}{2}$ yd

PLAN

• What is the problem asking you to find?

How _____ the dollhouse will be when the roof is attached

• What do you need to know to solve the problem?

What is the height of the dollhouse? _____ yard

What is the height of the roof? _____ yard

• How can you solve the problem?

You can add the height of the roof to the height of the dollhouse.

SOLVE — Find the sum.

$$\frac{1}{2} + \frac{1}{6} = \frac{\boxed{}}{\boxed{}} + \frac{1}{6} = \frac{\boxed{}}{\boxed{}}$$

Simplify.

$$\frac{\boxed{} \div \boxed{}}{\boxed{} \div \boxed{}} = \frac{\boxed{}}{\boxed{}}$$

To simplify, I need to divide the numerator and denominator by the greatest common factor.

CHECK — Use a fraction model.

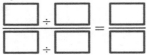

| $\frac{1}{2}$ | $\frac{1}{2}$ | + | $\frac{1}{6}$ | $\frac{1}{6}$ | $\frac{1}{6}$ | $\frac{1}{6}$ | $\frac{1}{6}$ | $\frac{1}{6}$ |

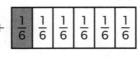

| $\frac{1}{6}$ | $\frac{1}{6}$ | $\frac{1}{6}$ | $\frac{1}{6}$ | $\frac{1}{6}$ | $\frac{1}{6}$ | + | $\frac{1}{6}$ | $\frac{1}{6}$ | $\frac{1}{6}$ | $\frac{1}{6}$ | $\frac{1}{6}$ | $\frac{1}{6}$ |

The dollhouse will be $\frac{\boxed{}}{\boxed{}}$ yard tall when the roof is attached.

PRACTICE

Use a common denominator to write equivalent fractions.

Use the problem-solving steps to help you. Include the units in your answer.

1 Hayden bought $\frac{7}{8}$ pound of grapes. He shared $\frac{1}{2}$ pound of grapes with his friends. What fraction of a pound of grapes does Hayden have left?

CHECKLIST
- [ ] READ
- [ ] PLAN
- [ ] SOLVE
- [ ] CHECK

2 Gabriella walked $\frac{2}{5}$ mile and ran $\frac{3}{10}$ mile. How far did Gabriella travel in all?

CHECKLIST
- [ ] READ
- [ ] PLAN
- [ ] SOLVE
- [ ] CHECK

3 Robert raked leaves for his neighbors. He raked leaves for $\frac{1}{2}$ hour on Tuesday and $\frac{1}{3}$ hour on Wednesday. How many hours in all did Robert spend raking?

CHECKLIST
- [ ] READ
- [ ] PLAN
- [ ] SOLVE
- [ ] CHECK

Fractions as Division

PLUG IN Dividing by One-Digit Divisors

To divide 492 ÷ 4 means to separate 492 into 4 equal groups. The **quotient** represents the number in each group. Divide each place-value part of the **dividend**, 492, by the **divisor**, 4.

1 Start with the hundreds place. Divide the 4 hundreds by 4. The 4 goes into 4 hundreds 1 time with 0 hundreds left over.

2 Divide the tens place. Bring down the 9 tens from 492. The 4 goes into 9 tens 2 times with 1 ten left over.

3 Divide the ones place. Bring down the 2 ones from 492. Along with the remaining 1 ten, there are 12 ones. The 4 goes into 12 ones 3 times with 0 ones left over. So there is no remainder.

4 Each equal group has 1 hundred, 2 tens, and 3 ones, or 123.

You can check your answer by multiplying the quotient by the divisor:

$$123 \times 4 = 492$$

↑

This matches the dividend. The answer is correct.

> There are enough hundreds in the dividend to divide by 4, so the first digit in the quotient goes in the hundreds place.

$$
\begin{array}{r}
123 \\
4\overline{)492} \\
\end{array}
$$

-4 ↓ ← $4 \times 1 = 4$

09

-8 ↓ ← $4 \times 2 = 8$

12

-12 ← $4 \times 3 = 12$

0 ← no remainder

Words to Know

dividend
the number to be divided

$18 \div 6 = 3$
↑
dividend

divisor
the number by which the dividend is divided

$18 \div 6 = 3$
↑
divisor

quotient
the answer in a division problem

$18 \div 6 = 3$
↑
quotient

DISCUSS How do you know if a division problem has a remainder?

There is 1 thousand left over, so I combine it with the 3 hundreds from the hundreds place.

A You can use long division to divide.

DO Divide: 5,328 ÷ 4

1. Divide the thousands.
2. Divide the hundreds.
3. Divide the tens.
4. Divide the ones. Check for a remainder.

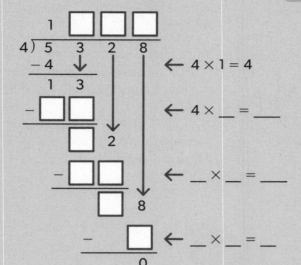

$$4 \times 1 = 4$$

$$4 \times \_\_ = \_\_$$

$$\_\_ \times \_\_ = \_\_$$

$$\_\_ \times \_\_ = \_$$

Divide ___5___ thousands by 4. There is _____ thousand left over.

Divide _____ hundreds by 4. There is _____ hundred left over.

Divide _____ tens by 4. There are _____ hundred left over.

Divide _____ ones by 4. There are _____ hundred left over.

Is there a remainder? _____

5,328 ÷ 4 = _____

PRACTICE

Fill in the digits in the boxes to complete the division.

1

```
    4 □ □
2) 8 7 4
  - 8
    0 7
    - □
      □ 4
    - □ □
        0
```

2

```
    □ □ □ R □
5) 6 0 7
  - 5
    1 0
   - □ □
       □ 7
     - □
       □
```

Multiplying Fractions by Whole Numbers

The fraction $\frac{3}{4}$ can be written as the sum of **unit fractions**.

$$\frac{1}{4} + \frac{1}{4} + \frac{1}{4}$$

$$\frac{3}{4} = \frac{1}{4} + \frac{1}{4} + \frac{1}{4}$$

You can write a fraction as the product of a whole number and a unit fraction.

Since multiplication is the same as repeated addition, the fraction $\frac{3}{4}$ is equal to 3 times $\frac{1}{4}$.

$$\frac{3}{4} = 3 \times \frac{1}{4}$$

Since $\frac{3}{4}$ is a product of 3 and $\frac{1}{4}$, it is also a **multiple** of $\frac{1}{4}$.

You can also multiply a whole number by a fraction without using repeated addition.

$$3 \times \frac{1}{4}$$

First, rename the whole number as a fraction with a denominator of 1.

$$\frac{3}{1} \times \frac{1}{4}$$

Multiply the **numerators** and multiply the **denominators**.

$$\frac{3}{1} \times \frac{1}{4} = \frac{3 \times 1}{1 \times 4} = \frac{3}{4}$$

I can think of $\frac{3}{4}$ as 3 groups of $\frac{1}{4}$.

$\frac{3}{4}$ is equivalent to $3 \times \frac{1}{4}$.

I get it! Since the denominator of any whole number is 1, the product will have the same denominator as the fraction.

Words to Know

unit fraction
a fraction with 1 as the numerator

$\frac{1}{2}$, $\frac{1}{10}$, and $\frac{1}{100}$ are all unit fractions.

multiple
the product of a number and another number

$$2 \times \frac{1}{8} = \frac{2}{8}$$
$$3 \times \frac{1}{8} = \frac{3}{8}$$
$$4 \times \frac{1}{8} = \frac{4}{8}$$

$\frac{2}{8}$, $\frac{3}{8}$, and $\frac{4}{8}$ are all multiples of $\frac{1}{8}$.

numerator
the top number in a fraction; tells how many equal parts are being considered

$\frac{3}{4}$ ← numerator

denominator
the bottom number in a fraction; tells how many equal parts there are

$\frac{3}{4}$ ← denominator

DISCUSS
What unit fraction would you use to show $\frac{3}{5}$ as the product of a whole number and a unit fraction? Explain.

A You can write a fraction as the product of a whole number and a unit fraction.

> **DO** Write $\frac{4}{3}$ as a product.

❶ Determine the unit fraction to use.

❷ Write the fraction as a sum of unit fractions.

❸ Write the repeated addition as multiplication.

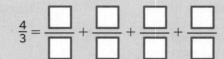

The denominator is ___**3**___. So, the unit fraction is $\frac{\square}{\square}$.

$$\frac{4}{3} = \frac{\square}{\square} + \frac{\square}{\square} + \frac{\square}{\square} + \frac{\square}{\square}$$

$$\frac{4}{3} = \underline{\hspace{1cm}} \times \frac{\square}{\square}$$

B You can multiply a whole number and a fraction.

> **DO** Multiply: $2 \times \frac{5}{6}$

❶ Rename the whole number as a fraction.

❷ Multiply the numerators.

❸ Multiply the denominators.

$$2 \times \frac{5}{6} = \frac{\square}{\square} \times \frac{5}{6}$$

$$= \frac{\square \times \square}{\square \times \square} = \frac{\square}{\square}$$

I remember! A whole number can be renamed as a fraction with a denominator of 1.

> **DISCUSS** Kym multiplied $5 \times \frac{1}{6}$ and found the product to be $\frac{1}{30}$. What can you tell Kym about her answer?

PRACTICE

Write the fraction as a product of a whole number and a unit fraction.

❶ $\frac{5}{2} = $ _____

❷ $\frac{3}{10} = $ _____

❸ $\frac{4}{8} = $ _____

Find the product.

❹ $2 \times \frac{1}{10} = $ _____

❺ $3 \times \frac{1}{2} = $ _____

❻ $8 \times \frac{1}{3} = $ _____

Fractions represent division, where the dividend is the numerator and the divisor is the denominator.

Juan has 2 pounds of popcorn to divide equally among 3 friends. He needs to find how much popcorn each person will receive.

You can use models to illustrate that $\frac{2}{3} = 2 \div 3$. Each whole represents 1 pound of popcorn. Divide each whole into 3 equal parts.

$\frac{1}{3}$	$\frac{1}{3}$	$\frac{1}{3}$	$\frac{1}{3}$	$\frac{1}{3}$	$\frac{1}{3}$

1 Person's Share

Each person receives $\frac{2}{3}$ pound of popcorn.

> I see! When the numerator is less than the denominator, the quotient is a fraction less than 1.

If Juan has 5 pounds of popcorn to divide equally among 3 friends, then the fraction that represents the quotient is $\frac{5}{3}$.

You can use division to rename the quotient as a mixed number.

$$5 \div 3 = 1 \text{ R2}$$

The whole-number part of the quotient is the whole-number part of the mixed number. The remainder is the numerator of the fractional part, with the divisor as the denominator.

$$5 \div 3 = 1\frac{2}{3}$$

Each person receives $1\frac{2}{3}$ pounds of popcorn.

> When the numerator is greater than the denominator, the quotient is a fraction greater than 1.

 DISCUSS Kevin has 5 pounds of dog food to share equally among 4 dogs. He said each dog will get $\frac{4}{5}$ pound of dog food. What can you tell Kevin about his solution?

LESSON LINK

PLUG IN

You can use long division to divide multi-digit numbers.

```
      1 3 4 R1
  7 ) 9 3 9
    − 7
      2 3
    − 2 1
        2 9
      − 2 8
          1
```

POWER UP

You can write any fraction as the sum of unit fractions or the product of a whole number and a unit fraction.

$$\frac{3}{12} = \frac{1}{12} + \frac{1}{12} + \frac{1}{12}$$

$$\frac{3}{12} = 3 \times \frac{1}{12}$$

GO!

> I get it! I can use what I know about fractions, mixed numbers, and division to solve real-word problems.

WORK TOGETHER

You can write a quotient as a mixed number.

- The division problem 84 ÷ 16 represents the situation.

- Divide 16 into 84.

- The quotient 5 R4 as a mixed number is $5\frac{4}{16}$.

There are $5\frac{4}{16}$ ounces of sports drink for each player.

A coach bought 84 ounces of a sports drink for 16 players. How many ounces of the sports drink are there for each player?

```
        5 R 4
  16 ) 8 4
      − 8 0
          4
```

If the quotient has a remainder, it can be written as a mixed number.

A You can write a quotient as a fraction less than 1.

DO A mother has 3 juice boxes to divide equally among her 4 children. How much juice does each child get?

❶ Set up a division problem.

❷ Write the quotient as a fraction with the dividend as the numerator and the divisor as the denominator.

❸ Interpret the quotient.

The division problem is _____ ÷ _____.

Write the quotient as a fraction: ▢/▢

Each child gets ▢/▢ of a juice box.

B You can write a quotient as a mixed number.

DO A tutor has 60 minutes to help 7 students. How much time is that per student?

❶ Set up a division problem.

❷ Divide.

❸ Write the quotient as a mixed number.

❹ Interpret the quotient.

The division problem is _____ ÷ _____.

```
        ▢ R ▢
  7 ) 6   0
    − 5   6
        ▢
```

_____ R _____ = ▢ ▢/▢

Each student has _____ minutes with the tutor.

DISCUSS Juanita is cooking 3 pounds of shrimp for 6 dinner guests. She figured that each guest will get 2 pounds of shrimp. Is she correct? Explain.

PRACTICE

Solve each problem. Write the quotient as a fraction or mixed number.

1 A museum is open for 8 hours each day. The manager schedules 12 tours for Tuesday. How long does each tour last?

$$\underline{\quad 8 \quad} \div \underline{\qquad} = \dfrac{\Box}{\Box}$$

Each tour lasts $\dfrac{\Box}{\Box}$ hour.

HINT
8 hours are divided equally among 12 tours.

2 Cassidy needs 6 pieces of ribbon of equal length for an art project. She has a ribbon that is 8 feet long. If she cuts it into 6 equal pieces, how long will each piece be?

$$\underline{\quad 8 \quad} \div \underline{\qquad} = \underline{\quad 1 \quad} R \underline{\qquad}$$

Each piece will be $\Box \dfrac{\Box}{\Box}$ feet long.

REMEMBER
The remainder can be written as the numerator of a fraction with the divisor as the denominator.

3 There are 15 members of the hiking club. Gilles made 7 pounds of trail mix to take on the next hike. How many pounds of trail mix does each club member get?

Each member gets $\dfrac{\Box}{\Box}$ pound of trail mix.

4 A pitcher holds 19 ounces of juice. Olga will pour it equally into 3 glasses. How much juice will each glass contain?

Each glass will contain $\Box \dfrac{\Box}{\Box}$ ounces of juice.

5 A dance teacher bought 9 yards of tulle to make 11 tutus. How many yards of tulle will be used to make each tutu?

Each tutu will be made from $\dfrac{\Box}{\Box}$ yard of tulle.

Solve each problem. Write the quotient as a fraction or mixed number.

6 Jana prepared 20 cups of punch for 9 people. How much punch per person is that?

Jana prepared _____ cups per person.

7 A baker has made 2 pounds of dough that he will form into 24 dinner rolls. How much dough will be used to make each dinner roll?

Each dinner roll will be made from _____ pound of dough.

8 A roast that weighs 5 pounds is divided into 12 equal pieces. How much does each piece weigh?

Each piece weighs _____ pound.

9 Donny is building a square frame out of a piece of wood that is 17 inches long. After he divides the wood into 4 equal pieces, how long is each piece?

Each piece is _____ inches long.

Solve. Write the quotient as a mixed number.

10 A carpenter will divide a board that is 80 inches long into 6 equal pieces. What is the length of each piece? _____

11 A painter has 35 minutes to paint 4 identical walls. How many minutes can he spend on each wall? _____

Remember: When there is a remainder, write the remainder as the numerator and the divisor as the denominator.

DISCUSS **Apply the Concept**

Corinna wants to divide 10 ounces of cheese equally among 4 hamburgers.

How can she find the right amount of cheese to put on each hamburger?

Each hamburger gets _____ ounces of cheese.

The quotient will be a mixed number.

PROBLEM SOLVING

PIZZA PARTY!

READ

Georgina has ordered 5 small pizzas for a pizza party. There will be 8 people at the party, including herself. Each pizza is divided into 8 slices. How many slices of pizza will each person get?

PLAN

• What is the problem asking you to find?

The number of _____ each person will get

• What do you need to know to solve the problem?

There are _____ pizzas and _____ people at the party.

Each pizza has _____ slices.

• How can you find the answer?

You can divide _____ pizzas by _____ people.

SOLVE

Write the division problem. _____ ÷ _____

Write the division as a fraction $\dfrac{\boxed{}}{\boxed{}}$

Each person gets _____ of a pizza.

Since each pizza is cut into 8 slices, each slice is $\frac{1}{8}$ of a pizza. The fraction $\frac{5}{8}$ is equal to _____ $\times \frac{1}{8}$. So, _____ $\frac{1}{8}$ parts is the same as _____ slices.

CHECK

Multiply to check your division.

First, multiply the number of slices each person will get, _____, by the fraction of a pizza that each slice represents, $\frac{1}{8}$.

_____ $\times \frac{1}{8} =$ _____

Now, multiply that fraction by the number of people. The result should be the total number of pizzas.

_____ $\times 8 =$ _____

Each person will get _____ slices of pizza.

Write a division problem to represent the situation.

PRACTICE

Use the problem-solving steps to help you.

1 Benny will cut a piece of fabric that is 2 yards long into 3 equal pieces. What is the length of each piece?

CHECKLIST
- [ ] READ
- [ ] PLAN
- [ ] SOLVE
- [ ] CHECK

2 One cup of medicine can be divided into 8 doses. How much medicine will be in each dose?

CHECKLIST
- [ ] READ
- [ ] PLAN
- [ ] SOLVE
- [ ] CHECK

3 Sanjay has 3 gallons of milk. He will put an equal amount into 4 pitchers. How much milk will be in each pitcher?

CHECKLIST
- [ ] READ
- [ ] PLAN
- [ ] SOLVE
- [ ] CHECK

4 Lupe has a 5-pound piece of clay. She will use it to make 9 identical pots. How much clay will be used for each pot?

CHECKLIST
- [ ] READ
- [ ] PLAN
- [ ] SOLVE
- [ ] CHECK

Multiplying Fractions

PLUG IN **Understanding Fractions as Multiples**

These models show the fraction $\frac{5}{3}$.

Since the numerator is greater than the denominator, this model shows 1 model completely shaded to represent $\frac{3}{3}$.

You can interpret $\frac{5}{3}$ as the sum of **unit fractions**.

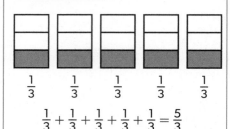

$$\frac{1}{3} \quad \frac{1}{3} \quad \frac{1}{3} \quad \frac{1}{3} \quad \frac{1}{3}$$

$$\frac{1}{3} + \frac{1}{3} + \frac{1}{3} + \frac{1}{3} + \frac{1}{3} = \frac{5}{3}$$

You can write a fraction as the product of a whole number and a unit fraction.

$$5 \times \frac{1}{3} = \frac{5}{3}$$

$\frac{5}{3}$ is a **multiple** of $\frac{1}{3}$.

Each model has 3 equal parts. There are 5 shaded parts.

I see! The models show 5 groups of $\frac{1}{3}$.

Right! Repeated addition relates to multiplication.

Words to Know

multiple	**unit fraction**
the product of a number and another number	a fraction with 1 as the numerator

DISCUSS Are the fractions $\frac{3}{5}$ and $\frac{5}{3}$ multiples of the same unit fraction? Explain.

A You can use models and equations to show a fraction as sum of unit fraction.

DO Show $\frac{5}{4}$ as a sum of unit fractions.

❶ Shade unit fractions to show $\frac{5}{4}$.

❷ Write an equation to show the $\frac{5}{4}$ as the sum of unit fractions.

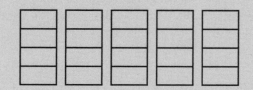

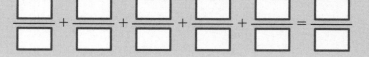

B You can write equations to show a fraction as a multiple of a unit fraction.

The unit fraction has the same denominator as $\frac{9}{8}$.

DO Show $\frac{9}{8}$ as a multiple of a unit fraction.

❶ Write an equation to show $\frac{9}{8}$ as the sum of unit fractions.

$$\frac{1}{8} + \frac{1}{8} + \frac{1}{8} + \frac{1}{8} + \frac{1}{8} + \frac{1}{8} + \frac{1}{8} + \frac{1}{8} + \frac{1}{8} = \frac{9}{8}$$

❷ Multiply the number of groups by the unit fraction.

There are _____**9**_____ groups of $\frac{\boxed{}}{\boxed{}}$.

❸ Write a multiplication equation.

$$\underline{} \times \frac{\boxed{}}{\boxed{}} = \frac{\boxed{}}{\boxed{}}$$

❹ Complete the sentence

$\frac{9}{8}$ is a multiple of $\frac{\boxed{}}{\boxed{}}$.

PRACTICE

Shade unit fractions to model the fraction.

1 $\frac{4}{3}$

2 $\frac{6}{4}$

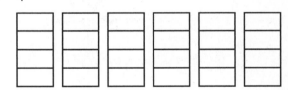

Write an equation to show the fraction as a sum of unit fractions.

3 $\frac{4}{3}$

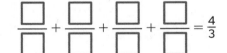

$$\frac{\boxed{}}{\boxed{}} + \frac{\boxed{}}{\boxed{}} + \frac{\boxed{}}{\boxed{}} + \frac{\boxed{}}{\boxed{}} = \frac{4}{3}$$

4 $\frac{3}{2}$

$$\frac{\boxed{}}{\boxed{}} + \frac{\boxed{}}{\boxed{}} + \frac{\boxed{}}{\boxed{}} = \frac{3}{2}$$

Write an equation to show the fraction as a multiple of a unit fraction.

5 $\frac{4}{8}$

$$\underline{} \times \frac{\boxed{}}{\boxed{}} = \frac{\boxed{}}{\boxed{}}$$

$\frac{4}{8}$ is a multiple of $\frac{\boxed{}}{\boxed{}}$.

6 $\frac{5}{7}$

$$\underline{} \times \frac{\boxed{}}{\boxed{}} = \frac{\boxed{}}{\boxed{}}$$

$\frac{5}{7}$ is a multiple of $\frac{\boxed{}}{\boxed{}}$.

Fraction Models can be found on p. 239.

Multiplying a Fraction by a Whole Number

You can use a model to multiply a fraction by a whole number.

$$5 \times \frac{2}{3}$$

Since $\frac{2}{3}$ is a multiple of the unit fraction $\frac{1}{3}$, you can rewrite the multiplication problem with the unit fraction.

$$5 \times \frac{2}{3} = 10 \times \frac{1}{3}$$

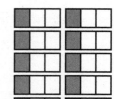

To find the product, rewrite the whole number as a fraction with a denominator of 1. Then multiply the numerators and denominators.

$$10 \times \frac{1}{3} = \frac{10}{1} \times \frac{1}{3} = \frac{10 \times 1}{1 \times 3} = \frac{10}{3}$$
$$5 \times \frac{2}{3} = \frac{5}{1} \times \frac{2}{3} = \frac{5 \times 2}{1 \times 3} = \frac{10}{3}$$

There are 5 groups of $\frac{2}{3}$.

There are 10 groups of $\frac{1}{3}$.

I get it! The product of the whole number and the fraction is the same as finding the number of unit fractions.

DISCUSS How is the number of unit fractions related to the numerator of the product?

A You can use models to find the number of unit fractions in a product.

DO Multiply: $3 \times \frac{3}{4}$

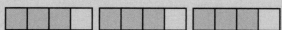

1 Find the unit fraction.

2 Shade the fraction models to show the unit fractions.

3 Determine the number of unit fractions.

4 Rewrite the multiplication problem with the unit fraction.

$\frac{3}{4}$ is a multiple of the unit fraction $\dfrac{1}{\boxed{}}$.

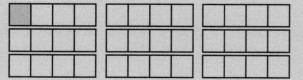

There are _____ groups of $\dfrac{1}{\boxed{}}$.

$$3 \times \frac{3}{4} = \underline{\quad} \times \frac{\boxed{}}{\boxed{}}$$

B You can multiply a fraction by a whole number.

 Multiply: $6 \times \frac{2}{5}$

① Rewrite the whole number as a fraction with a denominator of 1.

② Multiply the numerators.

③ Multiply the denominators.

④ Write the product.

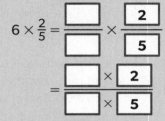

$$6 \times \frac{2}{5} = \frac{\boxed{}}{\boxed{}} \times \frac{\boxed{2}}{\boxed{5}}$$

$$= \frac{\boxed{} \times \boxed{2}}{\boxed{} \times \boxed{5}}$$

$$= \frac{\boxed{}}{\boxed{}}$$

The denominator stays the same because 1 times any number equals that number!

DISCUSS Addison multiplies $4 \times \frac{2}{3}$ and gets a product of $\frac{8}{12}$. What can you tell Addison about her answer?

PRACTICE

Use models to show the unit fraction and find the product.

1 $7 \times \frac{2}{3} = \dfrac{\boxed{}}{\boxed{}}$

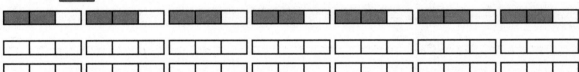

Find the product.

2 $2 \times \frac{2}{3} = \dfrac{\boxed{}}{\boxed{}}$

3 $3 \times \frac{3}{5} = \dfrac{\boxed{}}{\boxed{}}$

4 $7 \times \frac{2}{5} = \dfrac{\boxed{}}{\boxed{}}$

5 $8 \times \frac{2}{3} = \dfrac{\boxed{}}{\boxed{}}$

READY TO GO Multiplying Fractions

You can use a model to multiply two fractions to solve a real-world problem.

Sue designed a banner. She made $\frac{3}{4}$ of the banner purple. She put designs on $\frac{1}{3}$ of the banner that is purple. What fraction of the banner has designs on it?

This model represents the part of the banner that is purple.

You can separate the same model that represents the purple part of the banner into $\frac{1}{3}$ to find the fraction that has designs.

This model has been separated into 12ths. The overlap is the fraction of the banner with designs or the product.

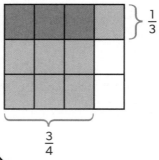

$\frac{1}{3}$

$\frac{3}{4}$

You can also write an equation to multiply two fractions. First, multiply the numerators. Then multiply the denominators.

$$\frac{3}{4} \times \frac{1}{3} = \frac{3 \times 1}{4 \times 3}$$
$$= \frac{3}{12}$$

Sue has put designs on $\frac{3}{12}$ of the banner.

> The model shows 3 shaded parts out of 4 and shows the fraction $\frac{3}{4}$.

> I see! Now 3 of 12 parts are shaded.

> I can find the product of 2 fractions using models or multiplication.

DISCUSS When you multiply $\frac{1}{3} \times \frac{2}{5}$, why is the denominator of the product 15?

LESSON LINK

PLUG IN

You can write a fraction as a multiple of a unit fraction.

$$\frac{1}{4} + \frac{1}{4} + \frac{1}{4} = \frac{3}{4}$$

$$3 \times \frac{1}{4} = \frac{3}{4}$$

POWER UP

You can find the product of a whole number and a fraction by rewriting the whole number as a fraction with a denominator of one and then multiplying the two fractions.

$$6 \times \frac{2}{5} = \frac{6 \times 2}{1 \times 5} = \frac{12}{5}$$

GO!

> I get it! Now I can multiply two fractions using models or by finding the product of the numerators and the product of the denominators!

WORK TOGETHER

You can use Fraction Models to solve a word problem that involves multiplying two fractions.

- The multiplication problem $\frac{1}{3} \times \frac{3}{5}$ represents the situation.

- The model shows $\frac{1}{3}$ of $\frac{3}{5}$ is equal to $\frac{3}{15}$.

- Multiply the fractions to get the product of $\frac{3}{15}$.

$\frac{3}{15}$ of the pizza has bell peppers.

$\frac{3}{5}$ of a pizza has tomatoes. Of that portion, $\frac{1}{3}$ has bell peppers. How much pizza has bell peppers?

$$\frac{1}{3} \times \frac{3}{5} = \frac{1 \times 3}{3 \times 5} = \frac{3}{15}$$

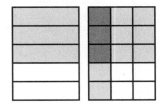

Multiply the numerators and denominators to find the product.

Fraction Models can be found on p. 241.

A You can multiply fractions to solve a word problem.

DO

Jessica bought $\frac{2}{5}$ pound of apples. Of those apples, $\frac{3}{7}$ are green apples. What fraction of the apples is green?

1 Write a multiplication problem to represent the situation.

2 Multiply the numerators.

3 Multiply the denominators.

4 Complete the sentence.

of the apples are green.

DISCUSS

Peggy drew this model to show $\frac{1}{3} \times \frac{2}{4}$. What can you tell Peggy about her model?

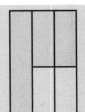

Remember that multiplication shows equal groupings. Does the rectangle show equal parts?

PRACTICE

Use models to multiply the fractions.

1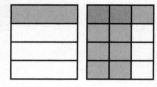

> **REMEMBER**
> Multiply both numerators and both denominators.

$$\frac{1}{4} \times \frac{2}{3} = \frac{\boxed{1} \times \boxed{}}{\boxed{} \times \boxed{}}$$

$$= \frac{\boxed{}}{\boxed{}}$$

2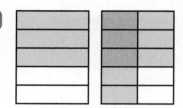

$$\frac{3}{5} \times \frac{1}{2} = \frac{\boxed{} \times \boxed{}}{\boxed{} \times \boxed{}}$$

$$= \frac{\boxed{}}{\boxed{}}$$

Shade the models and then multiply the fractions.

3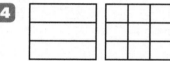

> **Hint**
> Group the numerators and denominators before multiplying.

$$\frac{5}{6} \times \frac{2}{3} = \frac{\boxed{5} \times \boxed{}}{\boxed{} \times \boxed{}}$$

$$= \frac{\boxed{}}{\boxed{}}$$

4

$$\frac{1}{3} \times \frac{2}{3} = \frac{\boxed{} \times \boxed{}}{\boxed{} \times \boxed{}}$$

$$= \frac{\boxed{}}{\boxed{}}$$

Multiply the fractions.

5 $\dfrac{7}{8} \times \dfrac{3}{4} = \dfrac{\boxed{} \times \boxed{}}{\boxed{} \times \boxed{}}$

$$= \frac{\boxed{}}{\boxed{}}$$

6 $\dfrac{6}{7} \times \dfrac{2}{4} = \dfrac{\boxed{}}{\boxed{}}$

Write a multiplication problem to represent the situation. Then solve.

7 Mr. Jones is planting roses in $\frac{3}{4}$ of his garden. He wants $\frac{2}{5}$ of the roses to be red. What fraction of the roses will be red?

8 One-fourth of a quilt is covered in blue squares. Of the blue squares, $\frac{2}{3}$ are light blue. What fraction of the quilt is covered in light blue squares?

9 In a shop, $\frac{3}{7}$ of the sweatshirts have white on them. Of these, $\frac{1}{4}$ also have blue on them. What fraction of the sweatshirts are both blue and white?

10 In a class, $\frac{1}{3}$ of the students have pets. Of these, $\frac{2}{9}$ have dogs. What fraction of the class has dogs?

Solve.

11 Brendan hiked $\frac{2}{5}$ of a trail one day. He hiked $\frac{3}{8}$ as far the next day. How much of the trail did Brendan hike the second day?

_____

12 Greta practiced her guitar for $\frac{3}{4}$ hour on Wednesday. She practiced $\frac{2}{6}$ as long on Thursday. How long did Greta practice on Thursday?

_____

Remember to group the numerators and group the denominators before multiplying.

DISCUSS → **Use Representations**

Denise drew this picture of a flag. She plans on drawing stars on the part with the darkest shading. How could she multiply fractions to find the fraction of her flag that will have stars?

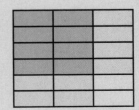

What fraction of Denise's flag will have stars? $\dfrac{\boxed{}}{\boxed{}}$

PROBLEM SOLVING

A TENNIS SHOES PROBLEM

READ In one class, $\frac{4}{5}$ of the students wear tennis shoes. Of those, $\frac{2}{3}$ have tennis shoes with shoelaces. What fraction of the class is wearing tennis shoes with shoelaces?

PLAN • What is the problem asking you to find?

The _____ of students who wear tennis shoes with shoelaces

• How can you solve the problem?

You can _____ the fraction of students who wear tennis shoes by the fraction of students who have tennis shoes with laces.

SOLVE The fraction representing the students with tennis shoes is $\frac{\square}{\square}$.

The fraction representing the students who have tennis shoes with laces is $\frac{\square}{\square}$.

Multiply the fractions to solve.

$$\frac{\square}{\square} \times \frac{\square}{\square} = \frac{\square}{\square}$$

CHECK Shade the models to check.

Write a fraction for the part with the darkest shading. $\frac{\square}{\square}$

$\frac{\square}{\square}$ of the students wear tennis shoes with shoelaces.

PRACTICE

Use the problem-solving steps to help you. Simplify the answer if necessary.

Simplify a fraction by dividing the numerator and denominator by the greatest common factor.

1 Martha bought 3 yards of fabric. She used $\frac{3}{4}$ of the fabric to make a tablecloth. What fraction shows the amount of fabric Martha used?

CHECKLIST
- [ ] READ
- [ ] PLAN
- [ ] SOLVE
- [ ] CHECK

2 Lenny has $\frac{6}{8}$ yard of a piece of wood. He uses $\frac{2}{3}$ of it to build a birdhouse. How much wood does Lenny use?

CHECKLIST
- [ ] READ
- [ ] PLAN
- [ ] SOLVE
- [ ] CHECK

3 Mary is decorating cookies. She uses blue sprinkles on $\frac{2}{5}$ of the cookies. She puts red sprinkles on $\frac{2}{4}$ of the cookies that have blue sprinkles. What fraction of the cookies has both blue and red sprinkles?

CHECKLIST
- [ ] READ
- [ ] PLAN
- [ ] SOLVE
- [ ] CHECK

11 Areas of Rectangles

PLUG IN — Using the Formula for Area of a Rectangle

The **area** (A) of a rectangle is the number of 1-unit squares needed to cover it with no gaps or overlaps.

5 squares

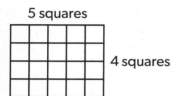

4 squares

There are 20 unit squares covering this rectangle.

You can use a **formula** to find the area of a rectangle.

$$\text{Area} = \text{length} \times \text{width}$$

$$A = l \times w$$

Multiply the length of the rectangle by the width.

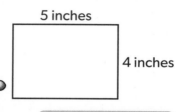

5 inches

4 inches

This rectangle has a length of 5 inches and a width of 4 inches.

Area is measured in **square units**.

$$A = 5 \text{ inches} \times 4 \text{ inches}$$

$$A = 20 \text{ square inches}$$

You can abbreviate square inches as sq. in.

I see! The area is equal to the number of square inches that cover the rectangle.

 Words to Know

area
the number of square units that cover a plane figure with no gaps or overlaps

formula
a special type of equation that shows a mathematical relationship

square unit
a unit used to measure the area of a plane figure

 DISCUSS

A rectangle has a length of 10 inches and a width of 3 inches. To find the area, Marlon multiplies 10×3 and Sari multiplies 3×10. Will they get the same answer? Explain.

A You can use a formula to find the area of a rectangle.

DO Find the area of the rectangle.

❶ Write the formula for area.

❷ Write an equation using the length and width of the rectangle.

❸ Multiply. Complete the sentence.

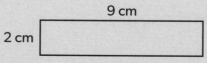
9 cm

2 cm

$A = \underline{\quad l \quad} \times \underline{\qquad}$

$A = \underline{\quad 9 \quad} \times \underline{\qquad} = \underline{\qquad}$

The area of the rectangle is _____ square centimeters.

B You can use the area formula to find the missing measure of a rectangle.

DO Find the missing measure.

① Write the formula for area.

② Substitute the area and the width of the rectangle into the formula.

③ Divide the area by the width.

④ Check by multiplying the width times the length.

I see! Since area is the product of the length and width, I can divide the area by the length or width to find the missing measure.

l

3 in. $A = 24$ sq. in.

$A = \underline{\hspace{1cm}} \times \underline{\hspace{1cm}}$

$\underline{\textbf{24}} = l \times \underline{\hspace{1cm}}$

$l = \underline{\hspace{1cm}} \div \underline{\hspace{1cm}} = \underline{\hspace{1cm}}$

Check: $\underline{\hspace{1cm}} \times \underline{\hspace{1cm}} = \underline{\hspace{1cm}}$

The length of the rectangle is $\underline{\hspace{1cm}}$ inches.

PRACTICE

Find the area of the rectangle.

1   12 mm

4 mm

$A = l \times w$

$A = \underline{\hspace{1cm}} \times \underline{\textbf{4}} = \underline{\hspace{1cm}}$

The area is $\underline{\hspace{1cm}}$ sq. mm.

2   7 feet

3 feet

$A = l \times w$

$A = \underline{\hspace{1cm}} \times \underline{\hspace{1cm}} = \underline{\hspace{1cm}}$

The area is $\underline{\hspace{1cm}}$ square feet.

Find the missing measures.

3   *l*

5 m $A = 30$ sq. m

$A = l \times w$

$\underline{\textbf{30}} = l \times \underline{\hspace{1cm}}$

$l = 30 \div \underline{\hspace{1cm}} = \underline{\hspace{1cm}}$

The length is $\underline{\hspace{1cm}}$ meters.

4   10 in.

w $A = 60$ sq. in.

$A = l \times w$

$\underline{\hspace{1cm}} = \underline{\hspace{1cm}} \times w$

$w = \underline{\hspace{1cm}} \div \underline{\hspace{1cm}} = \underline{\hspace{1cm}}$

The width is $\underline{\hspace{1cm}}$ inches.

You can use a model to multiply two fractions.

Multiply: $\frac{2}{3} \times \frac{1}{4}$

Start with a model for $\frac{1}{4}$. Then separate the same model into 3rds and show $\frac{2}{3}$ of the $\frac{1}{4}$.

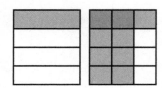

Now the model is divided into 12 equal parts. Each part represents $\frac{1}{12}$ of the whole. The overlap shows $\frac{2}{3}$ of $\frac{1}{4}$.

$$\frac{2}{3} \times \frac{1}{4} = \frac{2}{12}$$

You can also write an equation to multiply two fractions. First, multiply the **numerators**. Then multiply the **denominators**.

$$\frac{2}{3} \times \frac{1}{4} = \frac{2 \times 1}{3 \times 4}$$
$$= \frac{2}{12}$$

> I see! I can find the product of 2 fractions by multiplying the numerators and the denominators.

> When I multiply fractions, I am finding a fraction of another fraction.

Words to Know

denominator
the bottom number in a fraction that tells how many equal parts there are in the whole

$$\frac{1}{4} \leftarrow \text{denominator}$$

numerator
the top number in a fraction that tells how many equal parts are being counted

$$\text{numerator} \rightarrow \frac{1}{4}$$

DISCUSS

Antwan drew the model at right to show $\frac{1}{2} \times \frac{5}{6}$.

How does Antwan's model show the product of $\frac{1}{2} \times \frac{5}{6}$?

A You can multiply fractions without a model.

DO

Multiply: $\frac{4}{5} \times \frac{3}{8}$

1 Multiply the numerators.

2 Multiply the denominators.

3 Write the product.

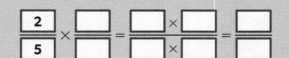

I get it! The solution to the problem is the product of the fractions.

B You can solve some real-world problems by multiplying fractions.

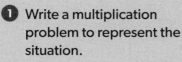

Three-fourths of the 5th-grade students ride the bus to school.
Two-fifths of the students who ride the bus are in an after-school club.
What fraction of 5th-grade students rides the bus and is in an after-school club?

1 Write a multiplication problem to represent the situation.

$$\frac{2}{5} \times \frac{\boxed{}}{\boxed{}} = \frac{\boxed{} \times \boxed{}}{\boxed{} \times \boxed{}} = \frac{\boxed{}}{\boxed{}}$$

2 Multiply the numerators.

3 Multiply the denominators.

_____ of 5th grade students rides the bus and is in an after-school club.

4 Write the product.

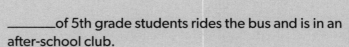

DISCUSS Rebecca said that to multiply $\frac{1}{4} \times \frac{2}{3}$, first she needs to change each fraction to an equivalent fraction with a common denominator. What can you tell Rebecca about her statement?

PRACTICE

Find the product.

1 $\frac{3}{4} \times \frac{2}{9} = \dfrac{\boxed{3} \times \boxed{2}}{\boxed{} \times \boxed{}} = \dfrac{\boxed{}}{\boxed{}}$

2 $\frac{5}{8} \times \frac{3}{7} = \dfrac{\boxed{} \times \boxed{}}{\boxed{8} \times \boxed{7}} = \dfrac{\boxed{}}{\boxed{}}$

3 $\frac{2}{3} \times \frac{5}{6} = \dfrac{\boxed{} \times \boxed{}}{\boxed{} \times \boxed{}} = \dfrac{\boxed{}}{\boxed{}}$

4 Kelly bought $\frac{7}{8}$ yard of ribbon. She used $\frac{2}{3}$ of the ribbon to trim a pillow.
What fraction of a yard did she use for the trim?

$\dfrac{\boxed{}}{\boxed{}}$ yard

Sometimes a rectangle has a length and width that are measured in fractions.

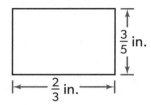

To find the area of a $\frac{2}{3}$ in. by $\frac{3}{5}$ in. rectangle, first divide the rectangle into sections with side lengths that are unit fractions.

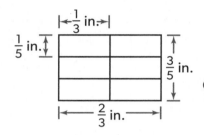

Think: $\frac{3}{5} = 3 \times \frac{1}{5}$
$\frac{2}{3} = 2 \times \frac{1}{3}$

Each section has a length of $\frac{1}{3}$ inch and a width of $\frac{1}{5}$ inch. Multiply to find the area of one section.

Area of 1 section: $\frac{1}{3}$ in. $\times \frac{1}{5}$ in. $= \frac{1}{15}$ sq. in.

Multiply the area of one section by the number of sections to find the total area of the rectangle.

Area of rectangle: $6 \times \frac{1}{15}$ sq. in. $= \frac{6}{15}$ sq. in.

I see! There are 6 sections. Each section has an area of $\frac{1}{15}$ square inch.

DISCUSS

Neela drew a model to find the area of a rectangle with length $\frac{5}{8}$ m and width $\frac{3}{4}$ m.

What would you tell Neela about her model?

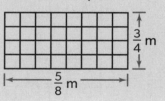

LESSON LINK

PLUG IN	POWER UP	GO!

You can multiply length times width to find the area of a rectangle.

Area = $8 \times 5 = 40$ sq. cm

You can find the product of two fractions by multiplying the numerators and the denominators.

$$\frac{3}{4} \times \frac{2}{9} = \frac{3 \times 2}{4 \times 9} = \frac{6}{36}$$

I see! I can multiply to find the area of a rectangle with fractional side lengths.

WORK TOGETHER

You can use a formula for the area of a rectangle.

- Substitute $\frac{3}{8}$ for the length and $\frac{2}{5}$ for the width into the formula for area.

- Multiply the numerators. Multiply the denominators.

The area of the rectangle is $\frac{6}{40}$ square inch.

Find the area of this rectangle.

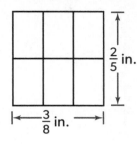

$$A = l \times w$$

$$A = \frac{3}{8} \times \frac{2}{5} = \frac{3 \times 2}{8 \times 5} = \frac{6}{40} \text{ sq. in.}$$

I remember! I can multiply the numerators and the denominators.

A You can find the area of a rectangle using the area formula.

DO Find the area of this rectangle.

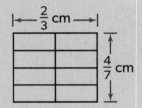

❶ Substitute the length and width of the rectangle into the formula for area.

❷ Multiply the numerators. Multiply the denominators.

❸ Write the area.

$$A = l \times w$$

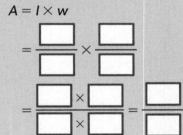

The area is ☐/☐ square centimeters.

Kayla and Shawn are finding the area of a rectangular table that is $\frac{2}{3}$ yard wide and $\frac{5}{6}$ yard long. Kayla draws a model with 10 sections, each measuring $\frac{1}{3}$ by $\frac{1}{6}$. Shawn multiplies $\frac{2}{3} \times \frac{5}{6}$. Will Kayla and Shawn get the same answer? Explain how you know.

PRACTICE

Find the area of the rectangle.

1

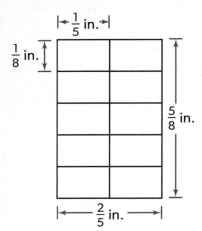

There are _____ sections.

Area of 1 section = $\dfrac{\square}{\square} \times \dfrac{\square}{\square} = \dfrac{\square}{\square}$

Total area = _____ $\times \dfrac{\square}{\square} = \dfrac{\square}{\square}$

The area of the rectangle is $\dfrac{\square}{\square}$ square inches.

2

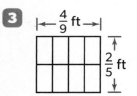

There are ___**9**___ sections.

Area of 1 section = $\dfrac{1}{5} \times \dfrac{\square}{\square} = \dfrac{\square}{\square}$

Total area = _____ $\times \dfrac{\square}{\square} = \dfrac{\square}{\square}$

The area of the rectangle is $\dfrac{\square}{\square}$ square meters.

> **HINT**
> The denominator of the side length is the denominator of the unit fraction.

3

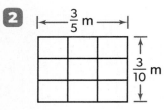

$A = l \times w$

$= \dfrac{\square}{\square} \times \dfrac{\square}{\square}$

$= \dfrac{\square \times \square}{\square \times \square} = \dfrac{\square}{\square}$

The area of the rectangle is $\dfrac{\square}{\square}$ square feet.

> **REMEMBER**
> First, multiply the numerators. Then multiply the denominators.

Find the area of the rectangle.

4
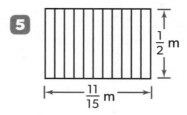
$\frac{2}{6}$ in.

$\frac{3}{8}$ in.

The area is ⬜/⬜ square inches.

5
$\frac{1}{2}$ m

$\frac{11}{15}$ m

The area is ⬜/⬜ square meters.

Solve.

6 A sign is in the shape of a square with a side length of $\frac{5}{12}$ meter. What is the area of the sign? Write the units in your answer.

_____

7 Alisha knit a baby blanket for her cousin. The blanket measures $\frac{7}{9}$ yard by $\frac{3}{4}$ yard. What is the area of the blanket? Write the units in your answer.

_____

I remember! A square is a rectangle with four equal sides. The length is the same as the width!

DISCUSS **Make the Connection**

The area will tell Brad how much space the wall covers.

Brad is painting a rectangular wall that is 3 meters high and $\frac{7}{10}$ meter wide. He needs to find the area of the wall to determine how much paint he will need.

How can Brad calculate the area of the wall?

What is the area of the wall?

PROBLEM SOLVING

APRIL'S QUILT

READ

April is making a quilt. The length of the quilt is 3 meters and the width is 2 meters. Each square of the quilt is $\frac{1}{3}$ meter long and $\frac{1}{3}$ meter wide. What is the area of the quilt?

3 m

2 m

PLAN

• What is the problem asking you to find?

The _____ of April's quilt

• What do you need to know to solve this problem?

What is the length of the quilt? _____ meters

What is the width of the quilt? _____ meters

• How can you solve the problem?

Use the formula for the area of a rectangle.

The formula is $A =$ _____ $\times$ _____.

SOLVE

Substitute the length and width of the quilt into the formula for area. Then multiply.

$A = l \times w$

$A =$ _____ $\times$ _____ $=$ _____ square meters

CHECK

Model the squares of the quilt. Find the area of each square, and multiply by the number of squares.

$\frac{1}{3}$ m

$\frac{1}{3}$ m

Number of squares: _____

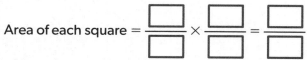

Area of each square $= \dfrac{\boxed{}}{\boxed{}} \times \dfrac{\boxed{}}{\boxed{}} = \dfrac{\boxed{}}{\boxed{}}$

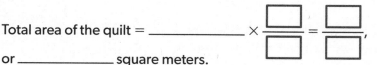

Total area of the quilt $=$ _____ $\times \dfrac{\boxed{}}{\boxed{}} = \dfrac{\boxed{}}{\boxed{}}$,

or _____ square meters.

The area of April's quilt is _____ square meters.

PRACTICE

Use the problem-solving steps to help you. Write the units in your answers.

1 A stained-glass window is made up of square pieces of glass. Each piece of glass has a side length of $\frac{3}{10}$ meter. What is the area of each piece of the stained-glass window?

CHECKLIST
- [ ] READ
- [ ] PLAN
- [ ] SOLVE
- [ ] CHECK

2 Andrew is making a table out of wood boards. Each board is $\frac{2}{3}$ yard long and $\frac{2}{15}$ yard wide. What is the area of each board?

CHECKLIST
- [ ] READ
- [ ] PLAN
- [ ] SOLVE
- [ ] CHECK

3 Mikayla is ordering fabric to make a wall hanging. The wall hanging will be $\frac{7}{8}$ foot long and $\frac{3}{4}$ foot wide. How much fabric will she need to make the wall hanging?

CHECKLIST
- [ ] READ
- [ ] PLAN
- [ ] SOLVE
- [ ] CHECK

I know! The amount of fabric is the same as the area of the wall hanging.

PLUG IN Multiplying Fractions

You can use a model to help you multiply a fraction times a whole number. To find $\frac{1}{2} \times 4$, show 4 wholes and separate each whole into 2 equal parts. Shade $\frac{1}{2}$ of each whole.

The shaded parts show the product.

To multiply without a model, write the whole-number factor as an **improper fraction** with a denominator of 1. Then multiply the numerators and multiply the denominators.

$$\frac{1}{2} \times 4 = \frac{1}{2} \times \frac{4}{1}$$
$$= \frac{1 \times 4}{2 \times 1}$$
$$= \frac{4}{2}$$
$$= 2$$

> I see! Four halves are shaded. Four halves equal 2 wholes. I got the same product when I multiplied!

You can multiply two fractions. To find $\frac{1}{2} \times \frac{4}{6}$, model each fraction.

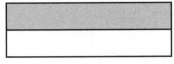

$\frac{1}{2}$

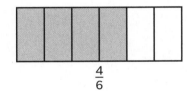

$\frac{4}{6}$

Combine the models to find the number of shaded parts in common. Four of the 12 parts have shaded parts in common. This shows the product $\frac{4}{12}$.

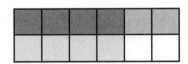

To multiply without a model, multiply the numerators and multiply the denominators.

$$\frac{1}{2} \times \frac{4}{6} = \frac{1 \times 4}{2 \times 6} = \frac{4}{12}$$

> The number of shaded parts in common is the numerator of the product. The denominator is the total number of parts.

Words to Know

improper fraction
a fraction with a numerator that is greater than or equal to the denominator
$\frac{5}{5}$ and $\frac{9}{5}$ are improper fractions.

DISCUSS How many parts would there be in a model that shows $\frac{1}{3} \times \frac{5}{8}$? How do you know?

Draw a model to check your answer.

A You can multiply a fraction by a whole number.

DO Multiply: $\frac{3}{4} \times 5$

① Write the whole-number factor as an improper fraction with a denominator of 1.

② Multiply the numerators.

③ Multiply the denominators.

④ Write the product.

$$\frac{3}{4} \times 5 = \frac{\boxed{3}}{\boxed{4}} \times \frac{\boxed{}}{\boxed{}}$$

$$= \frac{\boxed{} \times \boxed{}}{\boxed{} \times \boxed{}}$$

$$= \frac{\boxed{}}{\boxed{}}$$

B You can find the product of two fractions.

DO Multiply: $\frac{5}{6} \times \frac{1}{10}$

① Multiply the numerators.

② Multiply the denominators.

③ Write the product.

$$\frac{5}{6} \times \frac{1}{10} = \frac{\boxed{5} \times \boxed{1}}{\boxed{} \times \boxed{}} = \frac{\boxed{}}{\boxed{}}$$

PRACTICE

Use a model to multiply fractions.

1 $\frac{2}{5} \times \frac{1}{4} = \frac{\boxed{}}{\boxed{}}$

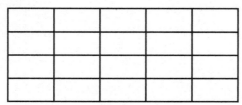

Find the product.

2 $\frac{7}{8} \times 3 = \frac{\boxed{}}{\boxed{}}$

3 $\frac{1}{5} \times 4 = \frac{\boxed{}}{\boxed{}}$

4 $\frac{1}{4} \times \frac{5}{6} = \frac{\boxed{}}{\boxed{}}$

5 $\frac{3}{8} \times \frac{1}{3} = \frac{\boxed{}}{\boxed{}}$

You can predict whether a product will be greater than or less than one of its factors.

$$\frac{1}{3} \times \frac{3}{5} = ?$$

Will the product be greater than or less than $\frac{3}{5}$?

The factors are $\frac{1}{3}$ and $\frac{3}{5}$.

The model below shows $\frac{3}{5}$.

This model shows $\frac{1}{3} \times \frac{3}{5}$.

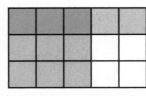

First I'll shade $\frac{3}{5}$. Then I'll shade $\frac{1}{3}$ of $\frac{3}{5}$.

Without multiplying to find the product, you can see that the product will be less than $\frac{3}{5}$.

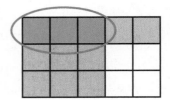

I see! The part that is circled is less than both factors.

DISCUSS Why is it useful to be able to estimate the size of a product?

A You can use a model to compare the product of two fractions to one of the factors.

DO Compare the product $\frac{1}{2} \times \frac{5}{6}$ to $\frac{1}{2}$. Write >, = or < to compare.

1 Use a model to show $\frac{1}{2} \times \frac{5}{6}$.

2 Circle the product in the model.

3 Write the correct symbol to compare the product to $\frac{1}{2}$.

$$\frac{1}{2} \times \frac{5}{6} \bigcirc \frac{1}{2}$$

I get it! The product of two fractions that are both less than 1 will always be less than both the factors.

> The product is a fraction or a part of 6.

B You can use a model to compare the product of a fraction and a whole number to one of the factors.

DO Compare the product $\frac{2}{3} \times 6$ to 6. Write >, =, or < to compare.

1 Use a model to show $\frac{2}{3} \times 6$.

2 Circle the product in the model.

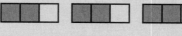

$\frac{2}{3} \times 6 \bigcirc 6$

3 Write the correct symbol to compare the product to 6.

DISCUSS Kaylee said that the product of $\frac{9}{10}$ and $\frac{1}{10}$ is greater than $\frac{1}{10}$. Is Kaylee correct? Explain.

PRACTICE

Circle the shaded parts in common. Then write >, =, or < to compare the product and a factor.

1 $\frac{1}{2} \times \frac{3}{4}$

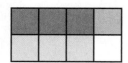

$\frac{1}{2} \times \frac{3}{4} \bigcirc \frac{3}{4}$

2 $\frac{1}{3} \times \frac{4}{5}$

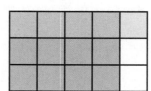

$\frac{1}{3} \times \frac{4}{5} \bigcirc \frac{4}{5}$

Circle the product. Then write >, =, or < to compare the product and a factor.

3 $\frac{3}{5} \times 4$

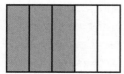
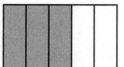

$\frac{3}{5} \times 4 \bigcirc 4$

4 $3 \times \frac{7}{8}$

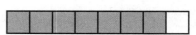
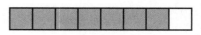

$3 \times \frac{7}{8} \bigcirc 3$

You can tell the size of a product based on the factors.

$\frac{2}{2}$ is equal to 1.

Multiply $\frac{2}{3} \times \frac{2}{2}$.

$$\frac{2}{3} \times \frac{2}{2} = \frac{2 \times 2}{3 \times 2} = \frac{4}{6}$$

$$\frac{2}{3} \qquad \frac{4}{6}$$

$\frac{4}{6}$ and $\frac{2}{3}$ are equivalent.

$$\frac{4}{6} = \frac{2}{3}$$

$\frac{1}{2}$ is less than 1.

Multiply $\frac{2}{3} \times \frac{1}{2}$.

$$\frac{2}{3} \times \frac{1}{2} = \frac{2 \times 1}{3 \times 2} = \frac{2}{6}$$

$\frac{2}{6}$ is less than $\frac{2}{3}$.

$$\frac{2}{6} < \frac{2}{3}$$

$\frac{3}{2}$ is greater than 1.

Multiply $\frac{2}{3} \times \frac{3}{2}$.

$$\frac{2}{3} \times \frac{3}{2} = \frac{2 \times 3}{3 \times 2} = \frac{6}{6} = 1$$

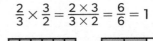

1 is greater than $\frac{2}{3}$.

$$1 > \frac{2}{3}$$

I see! Multiplying a fraction by 1 will give the same value as the fraction.

If I multiply a given fraction by a fraction less than 1, the product will be less than the given fraction.

If I multiply a given fraction by a fraction greater than 1, the product will be greater than the given fraction.

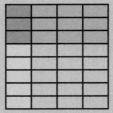

DISCUSS How would you prove to someone that $\frac{3}{5}$ and $\frac{6}{10}$ have the same value?

LESSON LINK

PLUG IN ➤ **POWER UP** ➤ **GO!**

You can use a model to find the product of two fractions, or you can multiply the numerators and the denominators.

$$\frac{3}{8} \times \frac{1}{4} = \frac{3 \times 1}{8 \times 4} = \frac{3}{32}$$

You can compare the product of two fractions to each factor.

$$\frac{2}{5} \times \frac{3}{4} = \frac{6}{20}$$

$$\frac{6}{20} < \frac{2}{5} \text{ and } \frac{6}{20} < \frac{3}{4}$$

I get it! I can compare the factors to 1 to find whether the product will be greater than, less than, or equal to each factor.

WORK TOGETHER

You can predict whether a product will be greater than or less than one of the factors.

- Compare the second factor to 1.

- Multiply the fractions.

The product of $\frac{5}{10} \times \frac{1}{4}$ is less than $\frac{5}{10}$.

Multiply: $\frac{5}{10} \times \frac{1}{4}$

The second factor is $\frac{1}{4}$. It is less than 1.

$$\frac{5}{10} \times \frac{1}{4} = \frac{5 \times 1}{10 \times 4} = \frac{5}{40}$$

$$\frac{5}{10} \times \frac{1}{4} < \frac{5}{10}$$

I remember! One whole is the same as $\frac{4}{4}$, and the second factor is $\frac{1}{4}$.

A You can predict whether the product will be greater than, equal to, or less than the first factor.

DO Multiply: $\frac{6}{8} \times \frac{5}{4}$

① Compare the second factor to 1.

② Multiply the fractions.

③ Write the correct symbol to compare the product to the first factor.

The second factor is $\dfrac{\boxed{}}{\boxed{}}$. It is _____ than 1.

$$\frac{6}{8} \times \frac{5}{4} = \frac{\boxed{} \times \boxed{}}{\boxed{} \times \boxed{}} = \frac{\boxed{}}{\boxed{}}$$

$$\frac{6}{8} \times \frac{5}{4} \bigcirc \frac{6}{8}$$

B You can predict the size of a product by comparing it to the factors.

DO Multiply: $\frac{4}{5} \times \frac{1}{3}$

① Compare the second factor to 1.

② Multiply the fractions.

③ Write the correct symbol to compare the product to the first factor.

The second factor is $\dfrac{\boxed{}}{\boxed{}}$. It is _____ than 1.

$$\frac{4}{5} \times \frac{1}{3} = \frac{\boxed{} \times \boxed{}}{\boxed{} \times \boxed{}} = \frac{\boxed{}}{\boxed{}}$$

$$\frac{4}{5} \times \frac{1}{3} \bigcirc \frac{4}{5}$$

DISCUSS Kane says that the product of $\frac{2}{8}$ and $\frac{6}{6}$ will be greater than $\frac{2}{8}$. What can you tell Kane about his reasoning?

PRACTICE

Compare the second factor to 1 and then multiply the fractions. Then write the correct symbol to compare the product to its first factor.

1 $\frac{7}{3} \times \frac{1}{2}$

$\frac{1}{2} \bigcirc 1$

$\frac{7}{3} \times \frac{1}{2} = \dfrac{\boxed{} \times \boxed{}}{\boxed{} \times \boxed{}} = \dfrac{\boxed{}}{\boxed{}}$

$\frac{7}{3} \times \frac{1}{2} \bigcirc \frac{7}{3}$

2 $\frac{9}{10} \times \frac{5}{5}$

$\frac{5}{5} \overset{=}{\bigcirc} 1$

$\frac{9}{10} \times \frac{5}{5} = \dfrac{\boxed{} \times \boxed{}}{\boxed{} \times \boxed{}} = \dfrac{\boxed{}}{\boxed{}}$

$\frac{9}{10} \times \frac{5}{5} \bigcirc \frac{9}{10}$

> **REMEMBER**
> Always check your answer!

3 $\frac{11}{12} \times \frac{2}{3}$

$\dfrac{\boxed{}}{\boxed{}} \bigcirc 1$

$\frac{11}{12} \times \frac{2}{3} = \dfrac{\boxed{} \times \boxed{}}{\boxed{} \times \boxed{}} = \dfrac{\boxed{}}{\boxed{}}$

$\frac{11}{12} \times \frac{2}{3} \bigcirc \frac{11}{12}$

4 $\frac{5}{12} \times \frac{5}{2}$

$\dfrac{\boxed{}}{\boxed{}} \bigcirc 1$

$\frac{5}{12} \times \frac{5}{2} = \dfrac{\boxed{} \times \boxed{}}{\boxed{} \times \boxed{}} = \dfrac{\boxed{}}{\boxed{}}$

$\frac{5}{12} \times \frac{5}{2} \bigcirc \frac{5}{12}$

5 $\frac{5}{8} \times \frac{1}{2}$

$\dfrac{\boxed{}}{\boxed{}} \bigcirc 1$

$\frac{5}{8} \times \frac{1}{2} = \dfrac{\boxed{} \times \boxed{}}{\boxed{} \times \boxed{}} = \dfrac{\boxed{}}{\boxed{}}$

$\frac{5}{8} \times \frac{1}{2} \bigcirc \frac{5}{8}$

6 $\frac{4}{3} \times \frac{2}{5}$

$\dfrac{\boxed{}}{\boxed{}} \bigcirc 1$

$\frac{4}{3} \times \frac{2}{5} = \dfrac{\boxed{} \times \boxed{}}{\boxed{} \times \boxed{}} = \dfrac{\boxed{}}{\boxed{}}$

$\frac{4}{3} \times \frac{2}{5} \bigcirc \frac{4}{3}$

Decide whether each prediction is correct or incorrect, and explain why.

7 Heath predicted that the product of $\frac{10}{4}$ and $\frac{3}{3}$ would be equivalent to $\frac{10}{4}$.

Is Heath's prediction correct? Explain.

_____

_____

8 Jane predicted that the product of $\frac{15}{9}$ and $\frac{2}{7}$ would be greater than $\frac{15}{9}$.

Is Jane's prediction correct? Explain.

I think Jane compared the wrong factor to 1!

_____

_____

9 Marcus predicted that the product of $\frac{1}{9}$ and $\frac{2}{2}$ would be less than $\frac{1}{9}$.

Is Marcus's prediction correct? Explain.

_____

_____

10 Maritza predicted that the product of $\frac{8}{3}$ and $\frac{10}{3}$ would be greater than $\frac{8}{3}$.

Is Maritza's prediction correct? Explain.

_____

_____

DISCUSS

Use Reasoning

Carlos says that all the products of the fractions below equal 1.

$\frac{9}{4} \times \frac{4}{9}$ $\frac{3}{5} \times \frac{5}{3}$ $\frac{2}{2} \times \frac{3}{3}$ $\frac{8}{5} \times \frac{5}{8}$ $\frac{1}{2} \times \frac{2}{1}$

Is Carlos correct? Explain how you know.

I can multiply the fractions to check my predictions.

PROBLEM SOLVING

A FRACTION OF TIME

READ

Olivia ran $\frac{3}{4}$ mile around a track. Andy ran $\frac{2}{3}$ the distance that Olivia ran. Was Olivia's distance greater than, equal to, or less than Andy's distance?

PLAN

• What is the problem asking you to find?

Compare the _____ Olivia ran to the _____ Andy ran

• What do you need to know to solve the problem?

Olivia ran _____ mile. Andy ran _____ the distance that olivia ran.

• How can you solve the problem?

Multiply to find Andy's distance and compare the two distances.

SOLVE

Multiply $\frac{3}{4} \times \frac{2}{3}$.

Compare the second factor to 1. $\frac{2}{3} \bigcirc 1$

Multiply the fractions.

$$\frac{3}{4} \times \frac{2}{3} = \frac{\boxed{} \times \boxed{}}{\boxed{} \times \boxed{}} = \frac{\boxed{}}{\boxed{}}$$

Compare the product to the first factor. $\frac{3}{4} \times \frac{2}{3} \bigcirc \frac{3}{4}$

CHECK

Shade the model to compare the distances Olivia and Andy ran.

Did you predict the answer? Was your prediction correct?

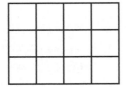

Olivia's distance around the track was _____ Andy's distance.

PRACTICE

Use the problem-solving steps to help you.

I know! I can use a model or multiplication to check my prediction.

1 Last week, Dwight read $\frac{5}{3}$ books. This week, he read $\frac{5}{6}$ as much as he read last week. This week, did Dwight read less than, the same as, or more than he read last week? How do you know?

CHECKLIST
- [ ] READ
- [ ] PLAN
- [ ] SOLVE
- [ ] CHECK

2 Becca is making 4 batches of muffins. Each batch contains $\frac{3}{4}$ cup of nuts. Does Becca need 4 cups of nuts, more than 4 cups, or less than 4 cups to make 4 batches? How do you know?

CHECKLIST
- [ ] READ
- [ ] PLAN
- [ ] SOLVE
- [ ] CHECK

3 Nate has finished $\frac{7}{8}$ of his homework. Vincent has finished $\frac{2}{2}$ as much homework as Nate has. Has Nate finished less, the same, or more of his homework than Vincent? How do you know?

CHECKLIST
- [ ] READ
- [ ] PLAN
- [ ] SOLVE
- [ ] CHECK

13 Multiplying Fractions and Mixed Numbers

PLUG IN Improper Fractions and Mixed Numbers

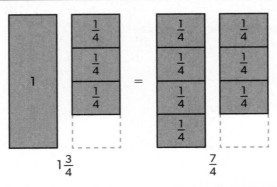

$$1\frac{3}{4} \qquad \frac{7}{4}$$

A **mixed number** has a whole-number part and a fraction part. You can use multiplication to rename $1\frac{3}{4}$ as an improper fraction.

To find the numerator of the improper fraction, multiply the whole-number part by the denominator in the fraction. Then add the numerator to the product.

Use the same denominator from the fraction part of the mixed number.

$$1\frac{3}{4} = \frac{(1 \times 4) + 3}{4} = \frac{7}{4}$$

In an **improper fraction**, the numerator is greater than or equal to the denominator. You can use division to rename $\frac{7}{4}$ as a mixed number.

Divide the numerator by the denominator.

$$\frac{7}{4} = 7 \div 4 = 1\,R3$$

The whole-number part of the quotient is the whole-number part of the mixed number and the remainder is the numerator of the fraction part. The denominator stays the same.

$$\frac{7}{4} = 1\frac{3}{4}$$

The numerator of this improper fraction is greater than the denominator.

I see! The fraction $\frac{7}{4}$ and the mixed number $1\frac{3}{4}$ are equivalent.

Words to Know

improper fraction
a fraction with a numerator that is greater than or equal to the denominator

$$\frac{5}{4}$$

mixed number
a number with a whole-number part and a fraction part

$$2\frac{3}{4}$$

How can you check your answer when you rename a mixed number as an improper fraction?

A You can rename a mixed number as an improper fraction.

DO Rename $2\frac{5}{9}$ as an improper fraction.

1 Multiply the whole number by the denominator.

2 Add the numerator to the product. Keep the same denominator.

3 Write the improper fraction.

$$2\frac{5}{9} = \frac{(\boxed{2} \times \boxed{}) + \boxed{}}{\boxed{}} = \frac{\boxed{}}{\boxed{}}$$

B You can rename an improper fraction as a mixed number.

DO Rename $\frac{15}{2}$ as a mixed number.

1 Divide the numerator by the denominator.

2 Write the whole number. Write the numerator. Keep the same denominator.

3 Write the mixed number.

I remember! The remainder is the numerator of the fraction part of the mixed number.

$$\frac{15}{2} = \underline{\quad 15 \quad} \div \underline{\qquad} = \underline{\qquad} \text{R} \underline{\qquad}$$

The mixed number is $\boxed{}\dfrac{\boxed{}}{\boxed{}}$.

PRACTICE

Rename as an equivalent mixed number or improper fraction.

1 $3\frac{1}{4} = \dfrac{(\boxed{3} \times \boxed{4}) + \boxed{}}{\boxed{4}} = \dfrac{\boxed{}}{\boxed{}}$

2 $\frac{12}{5} = \underline{\qquad} \div \underline{\qquad} = \underline{\qquad} \text{R} \underline{\qquad}$ $\qquad \frac{12}{5} = \boxed{}\dfrac{\boxed{}}{\boxed{}}$

Rename the mixed number as an improper fraction.

3 $5\frac{1}{2} = \underline{\qquad}$

4 $5\frac{3}{10} = \underline{\qquad}$

Rename the improper fraction as a mixed number.

5 $\frac{7}{6} = \underline{\qquad}$

6 $\frac{20}{3} = \underline{\qquad}$

POWER UP · Multiplying Mixed Numbers

You can multiply to find the product of two mixed numbers.

$$1\frac{1}{2} \times 2\frac{2}{3}$$

Rename the mixed numbers as improper fractions.

$$1\frac{1}{2} = \frac{(1 \times 2) + 1}{2} = \frac{3}{2}$$

$$2\frac{2}{3} = \frac{(2 \times 3) + 2}{3} = \frac{8}{3}$$

> I need to multiply the denominator by the whole number and then add the numerator.

Then multiply the improper fractions.

Multiply the numerators and multiply the denominators.

$$\frac{3}{2} \times \frac{8}{3} = \frac{3 \times 8}{2 \times 3}$$
$$= \frac{24}{6}$$

> I see! When I multiply two improper fractions, the result is an improper fraction.

The product is an improper fraction. You can rename the product as a mixed number by dividing the numerator by the denominator.

$$\frac{24}{6} = 24 \div 6 = 4$$

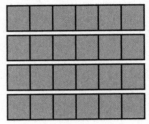

$$1\frac{1}{2} \times 2\frac{2}{3} = \frac{24}{6} = 4$$

> The product $\frac{24}{6}$ is equivalent to a whole number, 4!

DISCUSS How is multiplying two mixed numbers similar to multiplying two fractions less than 1? How is it different?

A You can multiply a mixed number by a fraction.

DO Multiply: $3\frac{1}{4} \times \frac{1}{2}$

① Rename $3\frac{1}{4}$ as an improper fraction.

② Multiply the fractions.

③ Rename the product as a mixed number. Divide the numerator by the denominator.

④ Write the product.

$$3\frac{1}{4} = \frac{(\boxed{3} \times \boxed{4}) + \boxed{}}{4} = \frac{\boxed{}}{4}$$

$$\frac{\boxed{}}{\boxed{}} \times \frac{1}{2} = \frac{\boxed{} \times 1}{\boxed{} \times 2} = \frac{\boxed{}}{\boxed{}}$$

$$13 \div 8 = \underline{} \text{ R} \underline{}$$

$$\frac{13}{8} = \boxed{}\,\frac{\boxed{}}{\boxed{}}$$

$$3\frac{1}{4} \times \frac{1}{2} = \boxed{}\,\frac{\boxed{}}{\boxed{}}$$

I rename both mixed numbers as equivalent improper fractions before I multiply.

B You can multiply a mixed number by a mixed number.

DO

Multiply: $4\frac{1}{2} \times 1\frac{2}{3}$

1 Rename the mixed numbers as improper fractions.

2 Multiply the improper fractions.

3 Rename the product as a mixed number.

$4\frac{1}{2} = \dfrac{(\boxed{} \times \boxed{}) + \boxed{1}}{2} = \dfrac{\boxed{}}{2}$

$1\frac{2}{3} = \dfrac{(\boxed{} \times \boxed{}) + \boxed{}}{3} = \dfrac{\boxed{}}{3}$

$4\frac{1}{2} \times 1\frac{2}{3} = \dfrac{\boxed{}}{2} \times \dfrac{\boxed{}}{3} = \dfrac{\boxed{} \times \boxed{}}{2 \times 3} = \dfrac{\boxed{}}{6}$

$\dfrac{\boxed{}}{6} = \boxed{} \div 6 = \boxed{} \text{ R } \boxed{} = \boxed{}\dfrac{\boxed{}}{6}$

DISCUSS

Zivia's work is shown below. What can you tell Zivia about her work?

$3\frac{3}{5} \times 2\frac{1}{2} = (3 \times 2) + \left(\frac{3}{5} \times \frac{1}{2}\right) = 6\frac{3}{10}$

PRACTICE

Multiply. If needed, rename the product as a mixed number.

1 $\frac{1}{2} \times 1\frac{1}{3} = \dfrac{\boxed{}}{\boxed{}}$

$1\frac{1}{3} = \dfrac{(\boxed{1} \times \boxed{3}) + \boxed{1}}{\boxed{}} = \dfrac{\boxed{}}{\boxed{}}$

$\frac{1}{2} \times \dfrac{\boxed{}}{\boxed{}} = \dfrac{\boxed{}}{\boxed{}}$

2 $1\frac{4}{5} \times \frac{2}{3} = \boxed{}\dfrac{\boxed{}}{\boxed{}}$

$1\frac{4}{5} = \dfrac{(\boxed{} \times \boxed{}) + \boxed{}}{\boxed{}} = \dfrac{\boxed{}}{\boxed{}}$

$\dfrac{\boxed{}}{\boxed{}} \times \frac{2}{3} = \dfrac{\boxed{}}{\boxed{}} = \boxed{} = \boxed{}\dfrac{\boxed{}}{\boxed{}}$

Multiply. Rename the product as a mixed number.

3 $2\frac{4}{5} \times 3\frac{2}{8} = \boxed{}\dfrac{\boxed{}}{\boxed{}}$

$2\frac{4}{5} = \dfrac{\boxed{}}{\boxed{}}$

$3\frac{2}{8} = \dfrac{\boxed{}}{\boxed{}}$

4 $3\frac{1}{2} \times 2\frac{3}{4} = \boxed{}\dfrac{\boxed{}}{\boxed{}}$

$3\frac{1}{2} = \dfrac{\boxed{}}{\boxed{}}$

$2\frac{3}{4} = \dfrac{\boxed{}}{\boxed{}}$

Multiplying Fractions and Mixed Numbers

Some real-world problems involve multiplying a fraction by a mixed number.

One batch of muffins requires $\frac{3}{4}$ cup of milk. How many cups of milk are needed to make $1\frac{1}{2}$ batches?

You can write an **equation** to represent the problem. The **variable** c represents the unknown value.

Let c = the number of cups of milk needed.

$$\frac{3}{4} \times 1\frac{1}{2} = c$$

I get it! I need to find how much is $1\frac{1}{2}$ times $\frac{3}{4}$ cup.

Find the value of c.

First, rename $1\frac{1}{2}$ as an improper fraction.

$$1\frac{1}{2} = \frac{(1 \times 2) + 1}{2} = \frac{3}{2}$$

Then multiply the fractions.

$$\frac{3}{4} \times 1\frac{1}{2} = \frac{3}{4} \times \frac{3}{2} = \frac{9}{8}$$

Rename $\frac{9}{8}$ as a mixed number.

$$\frac{9}{8} = 9 \div 8 = 1\,R1 = 1\frac{1}{8}$$

So, $c = \frac{9}{8}$, or $1\frac{1}{8}$.

I see! $1\frac{1}{8}$ cups of milk are needed to make $1\frac{1}{2}$ batches of muffins.

Words to Know

equation
a number sentence that shows that the values on both sides of the equal sign (=) are the same

$$1\frac{1}{2} \times \frac{1}{3} = \frac{1}{2}$$

variable
a letter or symbol used to represent an unknown value

$$1\frac{1}{2} \times \frac{1}{3} = n$$

↑
variable

DISCUSS   In the equation $1\frac{1}{2} \times \frac{1}{3} = \frac{1}{2}$, the product is less than the first factor. Explain why.

LESSON LINK

PLUG IN	POWER UP	GO!
You can rename a mixed number as an improper fraction, and vice versa. $$4\frac{2}{6} = \frac{(4 \times 6) + 2}{6} = \frac{26}{6}$$ $$\frac{26}{6} = 26 \div 6 = 4\,R2 = 4\frac{2}{6}$$	You can rename mixed numbers as improper fractions to multiply them. $$4\frac{2}{6} \times 1\frac{1}{2} = \frac{26}{6} \times \frac{3}{2} = \frac{26 \times 3}{6 \times 2} = \frac{78}{12}$$	I get it! I can use what I know about renaming mixed numbers and improper fractions to solve real-world multiplication problems.

WORK TOGETHER

You can write an equation to multiply two mixed numbers and solve a real-world problem.

- Rename the mixed numbers as equivalent improper fractions.

- Write an equation with a variable to represent the problem.

- Multiply.

- Rename the product as a mixed number.

The area of the flower bed is $4\frac{1}{2}$ square yards.

Find the area of this flower bed, in square yards.

$2\frac{1}{3}$ yd

| Flower Bed | $1\frac{3}{4}$ yd |

$1\frac{3}{4}$ yd $= \frac{(1 \times 4) + 3}{4} = \frac{7}{4}$ yd

$2\frac{1}{3}$ yd $= \frac{(2 \times 3) + 1}{3} = \frac{7}{3}$ yd

$A = \frac{7}{4} \times \frac{7}{3}$

$\quad = \frac{7 \times 7}{4 \times 3} = \frac{49}{12}$ sq. yd

$A = \frac{49}{12} = 49 \div 12 = 4\ R1 = 4\frac{1}{12}$ sq. yd

Right! The area of a rectangle is equal to the length times the width.

A You can multiply a mixed number by a fraction to solve a real-world problem.

DO

A bag contains $2\frac{1}{2}$ pounds of flour. Juan uses $\frac{1}{3}$ of the flour. How many pounds of flour did he use?

❶ Write an equation for the problem. Use the letter, p, as the variable.

❷ Rename the mixed number as an improper fraction.

❸ Multiply the fractions to solve for p.

❹ Complete the sentence.

Let $p = $ _____.

$2\frac{1}{2} = \dfrac{(\boxed{} \times \boxed{}) + \boxed{}}{\boxed{}} = \dfrac{\boxed{}}{\boxed{}}$

$p = \underline{} \times \underline{} = \dfrac{\boxed{}}{\boxed{}} \times \dfrac{\boxed{}}{\boxed{}} = \dfrac{\boxed{} \times \boxed{}}{\boxed{} \times \boxed{}} = \dfrac{\boxed{}}{\boxed{}}$

Juan used $\dfrac{\boxed{}}{\boxed{}}$ pound(s) of flour.

DISCUSS

How can you check your answer for a real-world problem that requires multiplying a fraction by a mixed number?

PRACTICE

Write an equation. Solve. If needed, rename the improper fraction as a mixed number.

1 Dayshawn bought $3\frac{1}{4}$ pounds of cheese. If $\frac{1}{2}$ of the cheese was cheddar, what is p, the number of pounds of cheddar cheese he bought?

REMEMBER
Use the variable that is given in the problem to write the equation.

$p = $ _____ $\times$ _____

$3\frac{1}{4} = \dfrac{(\boxed{} \times \boxed{}) + \boxed{}}{\boxed{}} = \dfrac{\boxed{}}{\boxed{}}$

_____ pounds

2 Leah is $5\frac{1}{2}$ feet tall. Leah's son's height is $\frac{2}{3}$ her height. What is s, her son's height, in feet?

HINT
Rename mixed numbers as improper fractions before multiplying.

$5\frac{1}{2} = \dfrac{(\boxed{} \times \boxed{}) + \boxed{}}{2} = \dfrac{\boxed{}}{\boxed{}}$

$s = $ _____ $\times$ _____

_____ feet

3 A painter uses $3\frac{3}{4}$ gallons of paint to cover one wall. She uses $1\frac{1}{2}$ times as much paint to cover a second wall. How many gallons, g, of paint does she use to cover the second wall?

_____ gallons

4 The distance across a swimming pool is $6\frac{1}{3}$ yards. If Ward swims back and forth across the pool $10\frac{1}{2}$ times, what distance, d, does he swim?

_____ yards

Write an equation to solve. Rename the product as a mixed number, if needed.

5 Henry practiced the flute for $4\frac{1}{6}$ hours last week. Georgia practiced for $\frac{1}{2}$ as long as Henry did. Let g represent the number of hours Georgia practiced. For how long did Georgia practice?

_____ hours

6 Karim is biking to his cousin's house, $7\frac{1}{2}$ miles away. So far, he has biked $\frac{3}{4}$ of the way there. Let m show the number of miles he has biked so far. What distance has Karim biked?

_____ miles.

7 Maddie bought $3\frac{2}{3}$ yards of blue ribbon. She bought $2\frac{1}{2}$ times as many yards of yellow ribbon. Let y represent the number of yards of yellow ribbon she bought. How many yards of yellow ribbon did she buy?

_____ yards.

Determine the area. Give your answer as an improper fraction and as a mixed number.

8

$2\frac{1}{8}$ ft

| Rug | $1\frac{1}{2}$ ft |

_____ or _____ square feet

Use the equation
$A = 2\frac{1}{8} \times 1\frac{1}{2}$
to find the value
of A.

DISCUSS

Think about Structure

A rectangular yoga mat is $2\frac{1}{2}$ yards long and $\frac{2}{3}$ yard wide. The equation for its area is given as $A = 2\frac{1}{2} \times \frac{2}{3}$.

Trey multiplies $\frac{5}{2} \times \frac{2}{3}$ to find the area. Karen multiplies $\frac{2}{3} \times \frac{5}{2}$ to find the area. If they both multiply correctly, who will find the correct answer—Trey, Karen, both, or neither of them? Explain.

PROBLEM SOLVING

HALF THE AMOUNT

READ A bread recipe makes two loaves and calls for $5\frac{2}{3}$ cups of flour. Vikram wants to make one loaf, so he uses $\frac{1}{2}$ as much flour. How much flour does he use? Write your answer as an improper fraction and as a mixed number.

PLAN • What is the problem asking you to find?

The number of cups of _____ used

• What do you need to know to solve the problem?

Two loaves call for _____ cups of flour. Vikram uses _____ as much flour.

SOLVE Write an equation. Let c = the number of cups of flour. $c = 5\frac{2}{3} \times \dfrac{\boxed{}}{\boxed{}}$.

Rename the mixed number: $5\frac{2}{3} = \dfrac{(\boxed{} \times \boxed{}) + \boxed{}}{3} = \dfrac{\boxed{}}{3}$

Multiply the fractions.

$$c = 5\frac{2}{3} \times \frac{\boxed{}}{\boxed{}} = \frac{\boxed{}}{3} \times \frac{\boxed{}}{\boxed{}} = \frac{\boxed{} \times \boxed{}}{\boxed{} \times \boxed{}} = \frac{\boxed{}}{\boxed{}}$$

Rewrite the answer as a mixed number.

$$\frac{\boxed{}}{\boxed{}} = \rule{1.5cm}{0.4pt} \div \rule{1.5cm}{0.4pt} = \rule{1.5cm}{0.4pt} \text{ R} \rule{1.5cm}{0.4pt} = \boxed{}\frac{\boxed{}}{\boxed{}}$$

CHECK Estimate the answer to check that it is reasonable.

$5\frac{2}{3}$ rounds up to 6. $\frac{1}{2}$ of 6 is _____. The value of c _____ close to that estimated answer.

So, it _____ reasonable.

Vikram used _____ cups of flour.

Rename mixed numbers as improper fractions before you multiply.

PRACTICE

Use the problem-solving steps to help you.

1 Leo has a gasoline can that holds $1\frac{1}{4}$ gallons of gasoline. Leo uses some of the gasoline to mow his lawn. Now the can is exactly $\frac{3}{4}$ full. How many gallons of gasoline are in the can now?

CHECKLIST
- [ ] READ
- [ ] PLAN
- [ ] SOLVE
- [ ] CHECK

2 One loop around the park is $3\frac{3}{4}$ miles long. Melinda runs around the park $2\frac{1}{2}$ times. What distance does Melinda run? Write your answer as both an improper fraction and a mixed number.

CHECKLIST
- [ ] READ
- [ ] PLAN
- [ ] SOLVE
- [ ] CHECK

3 Jasmine made a quilt with the length and width shown. What is the area of her quilt, in square feet? Write your answer as both an improper fraction and a mixed number.

CHECKLIST
- [ ] READ
- [ ] PLAN
- [ ] SOLVE
- [ ] CHECK

$6\frac{1}{2}$ ft

Quilt $2\frac{2}{5}$ ft

14 Dividing Unit Fractions and Whole Numbers

Tatyana has 5 cans of paint. Each can contains 1 gallon of paint. She uses $\frac{1}{4}$ of each can to mix a new color. How many gallons of paint does she mix?

Write an equation to represent the problem.

$$\frac{1}{4} \times 5 = p$$

The word "of" tells me to multiply.

You can use a model to represent the problem.

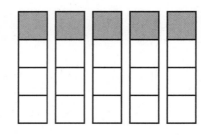

$$\frac{1}{4} + \frac{1}{4} + \frac{1}{4} + \frac{1}{4} + \frac{1}{4} = \frac{5}{4}$$

Each shaded section represents $\frac{1}{4}$ of a gallon. There are 5 shaded sections.

To solve the problem without a model, write the whole number, 5, as a fraction. Multiply the numerators and the denominators.

$$\frac{1}{4} \times 5 = \frac{1}{4} \times \frac{5}{1}$$
$$= \frac{1 \times 5}{4 \times 1}$$
$$= \frac{5}{4}$$

Tatyana mixes $\frac{5}{4}$ gallons of paint.

I get it! I can rename a whole number as a fraction by writing the whole number as a numerator over a denominator of 1!

 DISCUSS Ava drew this model to show $\frac{1}{4} \times 6$.

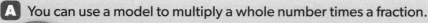

What can you tell Ava about her model?

A You can use a model to multiply a whole number times a fraction.

DO Multiply: $4 \times \frac{1}{3}$

1 Show 4 groups of $\frac{1}{3}$.

2 Add the shaded parts.

3 Write the product.

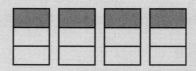

$$\frac{1}{3} + \frac{\square}{\square} + \frac{\square}{\square} + \frac{\square}{\square} = \frac{\square}{\square}$$

$$4 \times \frac{1}{3} = \frac{\square}{\square}$$

B You can multiply a whole number times a fraction without using a model.

 Multiply: $15 \times \frac{1}{10}$

① Rename the whole number as a fraction.

② Multiply the numerators and the denominators.

③ Write the product.

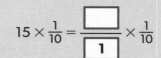

$$15 \times \frac{1}{10} = \frac{\boxed{}}{\boxed{1}} \times \frac{1}{10}$$

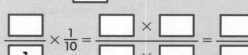

$$\frac{\boxed{}}{\boxed{1}} \times \frac{1}{10} = \frac{\boxed{} \times \boxed{}}{\boxed{} \times \boxed{}} = \frac{\boxed{}}{\boxed{}}$$

$$15 \times \frac{1}{10} = \frac{\boxed{}}{\boxed{}}$$

PRACTICE

Use the model to multiply.

1 $7 \times \frac{1}{4} = \frac{\boxed{}}{\boxed{}}$

2 $\frac{1}{6} \times 7 = \frac{\boxed{}}{\boxed{}}$

Multiply.

3 $6 \times \frac{1}{5}$

$$\frac{\boxed{}}{\boxed{}} \times \frac{1}{5} = \frac{\boxed{} \times \boxed{}}{\boxed{} \times \boxed{}} = \frac{\boxed{}}{\boxed{}}$$

4 $\frac{1}{3} \times 8$

$$\frac{1}{3} \times \frac{\boxed{}}{\boxed{}} = \frac{\boxed{} \times \boxed{}}{\boxed{} \times \boxed{}} = \frac{\boxed{}}{\boxed{}}$$

Fractions as Division

If 3 friends share 4 granola bars equally, what part of a granola bar does each friend get?

The division problem is: $4 \div 3$.

You can write the division problem as a fraction. The fraction bar in a fraction represents division. The value of a fraction is equal to its numerator divided by its denominator.

$$4 \div 3 = \frac{4}{3}$$

You can use a model to show $4 \div 3$.

Each whole represents 1 granola bar. Divide each whole into 3 equal parts.

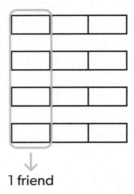

↓

1 friend

Each friend will get four $\frac{1}{3}$ parts.

$4 \times \frac{1}{3} = \frac{4}{3}$ of a granola bar

So, $4 \div 3 = \frac{4}{3}$.

You can use long division to find $\frac{4}{3}$.

$$3\overline{)4} \quad \begin{array}{r} 1 \text{ R1} \\ -3 \\ \hline 1 \end{array}$$

To write the quotient as a **mixed number**, write the whole number, 1, and write the **remainder** as the numerator of a fraction with the **divisor** as the denominator.

remainder $\rightarrow \frac{1}{3}$
divisor $\rightarrow$

So, $4 \div 3 = 1\frac{1}{3}$, and each friend gets $1\frac{1}{3}$ granola bars.

> I see! A fraction is another way to write a division problem!

> The dividend is greater than the divisor, so the quotient is a fraction that is greater than 1!

> A fraction greater than 1 can be written as a mixed number.

Words to Know

mixed number
a number that has a whole-number part and a fraction part

$1\frac{1}{6}$ is a mixed number.

remainder
the amount that is left over after division is complete

$$5 \div 3 = 1 \text{ R2}$$

divisor
a number by which another number is divided

$$5 \div 3 = 1 \text{ R2}$$

DISCUSS Ella drew a model to show that $3 \div 8 = \frac{3}{8}$. What can you tell Ella about her model?

A You can show division with quotients less than 1 as a fraction.

DO

Five friends equally share 4 quarts of water. How many quarts of water does each friend get?

1 Set up a division problem.

The division problem is ___4___ ÷ ___5___.

2 Write the quotient as a fraction with the dividend as the numerator and the divisor as the denominator.

$$\underline{\hspace{1cm}} \div \underline{\hspace{1cm}} = \dfrac{\Box}{\Box}$$

3 Interpret the quotient.

Each friend will get $\dfrac{\Box}{\Box}$ quart of water.

B You can show division with quotients greater than 1 as a fraction.

DO

Three sisters equally share the driving for a 10-hour trip. For how many hours does each sister drive?

1 Set up a division problem.

The division problem is _____ ÷ _____.

2 Divide to write the fraction as a mixed number.

3 Interpret the quotient.

$$\begin{array}{r} 3 \text{ R } \Box \\ 3\overline{)10} \\ -\underline{9} \\ \Box \end{array}$$

$$10 \div 3 = \Box\,\dfrac{\Box}{\Box}$$

Each sister will drive for _____ hours.

I see! Since the numerator is greater than the denominator, I can divide to write the fraction as a mixed number!

DISCUSS Keisha wants to write the fraction $\dfrac{25}{8}$ as division. Which number should she write as the divisor? Which number should she write as the dividend?

PRACTICE

Solve.

1 Six friends equally share a bag of popcorn. The bag contains 9 cups of popcorn. How many cups of popcorn should each friend get?

_____

2 Charlotte cuts a 3-foot-long piece of ribbon into 4 equal pieces to trim a square pillow. How long is each piece of ribbon?

_____

Dividing Unit Fractions and Whole Numbers

You can use models to help you divide a **unit fraction** by a whole number.

To divide $\frac{1}{2} \div 4$, start with a model for $\frac{1}{2}$.

Divide into 4 equal parts. Each part is $\frac{1}{8}$.

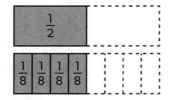

To divide without a model, multiply the dividend by the **reciprocal** of the divisor.

$$\frac{1}{2} \div 4 = \frac{1}{2} \div \frac{4}{1} = \frac{1}{2} \times \frac{1}{4} = \frac{1 \times 1}{2 \times 4} = \frac{1}{8}$$

When dividing a fraction by a whole number, the quotient is less than the dividend and the divisor.

You can also use a model to divide a whole number by a unit fraction.

To divide $2 \div \frac{1}{3}$, start with a model for 2 wholes. Divide each whole into 3 equal parts, or thirds. There are a total of 6 equal parts.

Multiply the dividend by the reciprocal of the divisor.

$$2 \div \frac{1}{3} = \frac{2}{1} \times \frac{3}{1} = \frac{2 \times 3}{1 \times 1} = \frac{6}{1} = 6$$

When dividing a whole number by a fraction, the quotient is greater than the dividend and the divisor.

 Words to Know

unit fraction
a fraction with 1 as the numerator
$\frac{1}{2}, \frac{1}{3}, \frac{1}{4}$, and $\frac{1}{5}$ are unit fractions.

reciprocal
a number that gives a product of 1 when multiplied by a second number
4 and $\frac{1}{4}$ are reciprocals: $4 \times \frac{1}{4} = 1$.

DISCUSS Morgan divides 5 by a number and gets an answer of 20. Bethany says that Morgan's answer is incorrect because the quotient should always be less than the dividend. What can you say to Bethany?

LESSON LINK

PLUG IN

You can use a model to multiply a fraction by a whole number.

$$3 \times \frac{1}{5} = \frac{3}{5}$$

POWER UP

You can show a fraction as division of the numerator by the denominator.

$$\frac{2}{5} = 2 \div 5$$

GO!

I get it! I can use what I know about multiplying and dividing fractions and whole numbers to solve problems.

How many $\frac{1}{2}$-cup servings are there in 3 cups of rice?

3 cups

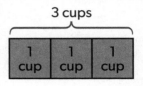

① The equation $3 \div \frac{1}{2} = n$ represents the problem.

② Solve for n.

Rename the whole number as a fraction: $3 = \frac{3}{1}$

Write the reciprocal of the divisor: $\frac{1}{2} \rightarrow \frac{2}{1}$

Rewrite as multiplication: $\frac{3}{1} \times \frac{2}{1} = \frac{6}{1} = 6$

So, $n = 6$.

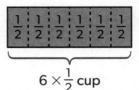

$6 \times \frac{1}{2}$ cup

③ Use multiplication to check.

$3 \div \frac{1}{2} = n$ is related to $n \times \frac{1}{2} = 3$.

$6 \times \frac{1}{2} = \frac{6}{1} \times \frac{1}{2} = \frac{6}{2} = 3$ ✓

I remember! To write the reciprocal of a fraction, switch the numerator and the denominator.

④ The models show 3 cups. Each cup is divided into 2 equal parts, or halves. There are 6 equal $\frac{1}{2}$ parts.

There are six $\frac{1}{2}$-cup servings of rice in 3 cups of rice.

A You can use multiplication to divide a whole number by a fraction.

DO

Divide: $2 \div \frac{1}{5}$

① Rename the whole number as a fraction.

② Write the reciprocal of the divisor.

③ Rewrite as multiplication. Write the quotient.

④ Multiply to check.

$2 = \dfrac{2}{\boxed{}}$ $\dfrac{1}{5} \rightarrow \dfrac{\boxed{}}{\boxed{}}$

$\dfrac{2}{\boxed{}} \times \dfrac{\boxed{}}{\boxed{}} = \dfrac{2 \times \boxed{}}{\boxed{} \times \boxed{}} = \dfrac{\boxed{}}{\boxed{}} = \underline{}$

Check: $\underline{} \times \dfrac{1}{5} = \dfrac{\boxed{}}{\boxed{}} \times \dfrac{1}{5} = \dfrac{\boxed{}}{\boxed{}} = \underline{}$

DISCUSS   Wes divided $\frac{1}{8}$ by 3 and got a quotient of $\frac{1}{24}$. Wes checked his answer by multiplying the quotient by the divisor. How will Wes know if he divided correctly?

PRACTICE

Use models to solve.

1 $\frac{1}{4} \div 3 = \dfrac{\boxed{}}{\boxed{}}$

| $\frac{1}{4}$ | | | |

2 $6 \div \frac{1}{4} =$ _____

| 1 | 1 | 1 | 1 | 1 | 1 |

Divide.

3 $\frac{1}{5} \div 3 = \dfrac{\boxed{}}{\boxed{}}$

4 $4 \div \frac{1}{7} =$ _____

5 $2 \div \frac{1}{9} =$ _____

Write an equation to solve. Use multiplication to check.

6 How many $\frac{1}{8}$-foot-long tiles must Isobel place in a row if she wants the row to be 3 feet long?

_____ ÷ _____ = _____

_____ tiles

7 If 6 people equally share $\frac{1}{2}$ gallon of milk, how much milk will each person receive?

_____ ÷ _____ = _____

_____ gallon(s)

Solve.

8 Craig used $\frac{1}{4}$ cup of sugar to make 12 cookies. How much sugar was in each cookie? _____

9 Megan bought 4 ounces of cheese. The cheese was cut into $\frac{1}{3}$-ounce slices. How many slices of cheese did she buy? _____

I know! I can write an equation to solve each problem.

 Check That It's Reasonable

Olivia divided 6 by $\frac{1}{2}$ and got a quotient of 3.

Is Olivia's quotient less than or greater than the dividend, 6?

When you divide a whole number by a unit fraction, you are finding the number of pieces in the whole number. Should the quotient be less than or greater than the whole number?

What error did Olivia make when she divided 6 by $\frac{1}{2}$?

What is 6 divided by $\frac{1}{2}$?

PROBLEM SOLVING

RIBBON CUTTING

READ

Kara needs 16 pieces of ribbon for a quilt. She cut a 3-foot-long red ribbon into $\frac{1}{6}$-foot-long pieces. Does she have enough pieces of ribbon?

PLAN

- What is the problem asking you to find?

    Whether Kara has enough _____ of ribbon

- What do you need to know to solve this problem?

    The length of the red ribbon is _____ feet.

    The length of each piece is _____ foot.

- How can you solve the problem?

    Divide the length of the _____ by the length of the _____.

SOLVE

Write an equation. Let r = the number of pieces of ribbon.

$$\text{_____} \div \frac{\boxed{}}{\boxed{}} = r$$

Solve.

$$\frac{\boxed{}}{\boxed{}} \times \frac{\boxed{}}{\boxed{}} = \frac{\boxed{} \times \boxed{}}{\boxed{} \times \boxed{}} = \frac{\boxed{}}{\boxed{}}$$

$r =$ _____

There are _____ pieces of red ribbon.

CHECK

Multiply the number of pieces of ribbon by the length of each piece. The product should equal the length of the ribbon before it was cut.

$$\text{_____} \times \frac{\boxed{}}{\boxed{}} = \frac{\boxed{}}{\boxed{}} \times \frac{\boxed{}}{\boxed{}} = \frac{\boxed{} \times \boxed{}}{\boxed{} \times \boxed{}} = \frac{\boxed{}}{\boxed{}} = \text{_____ feet}$$

Does Kara have enough pieces of ribbon? _____

Rewrite division as multiplication using the reciprocal of the divisor.

PRACTICE

Use the problem-solving steps to help you.

1 Max ran a total of 5 miles around a track. Each lap was $\frac{1}{8}$ mile. Zachary ran 36 laps around the track. Who ran more laps?

CHECKLIST
- [ ] READ
- [ ] PLAN
- [ ] SOLVE
- [ ] CHECK

2 Last month, Laurie practiced piano for $\frac{1}{4}$ hour each day for a total of 4 hours. Alisha practiced piano on 15 days. Who practiced on more days?

CHECKLIST
- [ ] READ
- [ ] PLAN
- [ ] SOLVE
- [ ] CHECK

3 Jervaise needs to make 20 sandwiches for a party. He has 6 pounds of turkey and he is using $\frac{1}{3}$ pound of turkey for each sandwich. Will he make enough sandwiches?

CHECKLIST
- [ ] READ
- [ ] PLAN
- [ ] SOLVE
- [ ] CHECK

Converting Measurements

PLUG IN Units of Measurement

The **customary system of measurement** is used to measure quantities.

- Length, or distance, is measured using inches (in.), feet (ft) and yards (yd).

- Weight, or how heavy an object is, is measured using pounds (lb) and ounces (oz).

- Capacity, or the amount of fluid an object can hold, is measured using cups (c), pints (pt), quarts (qt), and gallons (gal).

A comparison can relate equivalent quantities that use different units of measure. For example, 1 gallon is 4 times more liquid than 1 quart.

Time is measured using seconds (sec), minutes (min), and hours (hr).

The **metric system of measurement** is also used to measure quantities.

- Length is measured using centimeters (cm), meters (m), or kilometers (km).

- Capacity is measured using milliliters (mL) or liters (L).

- Mass, or the amount of matter in an object, is measured using grams (g) or kilograms (kg).

A comparison can relate equivalent quantities that use different units of measure. For example, 1 liter is 1,000 times more liquid than 1 milliliter.

> I see! The quantities are equivalent but the units of measure are different.

> There are small units of measure and large units of measure. Both can be used to measure the same object.

 Words to Know

customary system of measurement
a system of units of measure used in the United States

metric system of measurement
a system of units of measure most commonly used throughout the world

DISCUSS Which unit of measure is smaller, grams or kilograms? How do you know?

Customary and Metric Units can be found on p. 249.

A You can compare equivalent customary units of measure.

 DO Compare ounces and pounds.

1. Decide which unit of measure is heavier.

2. Complete the comparison.

___**Pounds**___ are heavier than _____.

1 pound is _____ times as heavy as 1 ounce.

B You can compare equivalent metric units of measure.

DO

Compare meters and centimeters.

Determine how many centimeters equal 1 meter.

1 Decide which unit of measure is shorter.

_____ are shorter than _____**meters**_____.

2 Complete the comparison.

1 centimeter is _____ times shorter than 1 meter.

PRACTICE

Complete each comparison. Use Math Tool: Customary and Metric Units to help you.

1 1 minute is _____**60**_____ times as long as 1 second.

2 1 quart is _____ times more liquid than 1 pint.

3 1 _____ is 12 times as long as 1 inch.

4 1 _____ is 60 times as long as 1 minute.

5 1 cup is 2 times less liquid than 1 _____.

6 1 inch is 36 times shorter than 1 _____.

7 1 kilogram is _____ times as heavy as 1 gram.

8 1 kilometer is _____ times as long as 1 meter.

9 1 _____ is 1,000 times as much liquid as 1 milliliter.

10 1 _____ is 100 times as long as 1 centimeter.

11 1 meter is 1,000 times shorter than 1 _____.

12 1 milliliter is 1,000 times less liquid than 1 _____.

Customary and Metric Units can be found on p. 249.

Multiply: 16 × 314

1. Set up the problem vertically. Line up digits with the same place value.

2. Multiply the ones, tens, hundreds in 314 by the 6 ones in 16. Regroup as necessary.

3. Multiply the ones, tens, hundreds in 314 by the 1 ten in 16.

4. Add the partial products.

16 × 314 = 5,024

$$
\begin{array}{r}
\overset{2}{3}14 \\
\times\ \ 16 \\
\hline
1,884 \\
+\ 3,140 \\
\hline
5,024
\end{array}
$$

← 314 × 6
← 314 × 10

I see! I need to regroup when the product of two digits is a 2-digit number.

Divide: 1,980 ÷ 12

1. Set up the problem using long division.

2. There are not enough thousands to divide by 12, so the first digit of the quotient is in the hundreds place.

3. Divide the hundreds, tens, and ones.

1,980 ÷ 12 = 165

I divide, multiply, and subtract in each step.

$$
\begin{array}{r}
165 \\
12\overline{)1980} \\
-12\ \downarrow \\
\hline
78 \\
-72\ \downarrow \\
\hline
60 \\
-60 \\
\hline
0
\end{array}
$$

← 1 × 12
← 6 × 12
← 5 × 12

DISCUSS   When do you regroup when multiplying?

A You can write a multiplication problem vertically to find a product.

DO   Multiply: 2,845 × 3

1. Set up the problem vertically. Line up digits with the same place value.

2. Multiply the ones, tens, hundreds, and thousands.

3. Regroup as necessary.

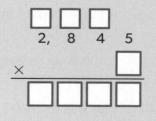

2,845 × 3 = _____

B You can use long division to find a quotient.

DO

Divide: 1,080 ÷ 60

1 Set up the problem using long division.

2 Decide where to place the first digit in the quotient.

3 Divide the tens and ones.

There are not enough thousands or hundreds to divide by 60, so the first digit in the quotient is in the tens place.

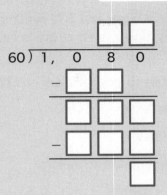

$$60 \overline{)\,1{,}080}$$

1,080 ÷ 60 = _____

DISCUSS When dividing, what should you do when there is a 0 in the dividend? Explain.

PRACTICE

Fill in the boxes to complete the multiplication or division.

1
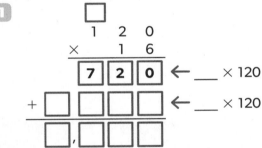

$$\begin{array}{r} \square \\ 1\ 2\ 0 \\ \times \quad 1\ 6 \\ \hline \boxed{7}\ \boxed{2}\ \boxed{0} \leftarrow \underline{\ \ } \times 120 \\ + \square\ \square\ \square\ \square \leftarrow \underline{\ \ } \times 120 \\ \hline \square,\square\ \square\ \square \end{array}$$

2
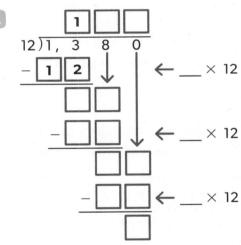

$$\begin{array}{r} \boxed{1}\ \square\ \square \\ 12 \overline{)\,1{,}380} \\ -\ \boxed{1}\ \boxed{2} \qquad \leftarrow \underline{\ \ } \times 12 \\ \hline \square\ \square \\ -\ \square\ \square \qquad \leftarrow \underline{\ \ } \times 12 \\ \hline \square\ \square \\ -\ \square\ \square \leftarrow \underline{\ \ } \times 12 \\ \hline \square \end{array}$$

Multiply or divide.

3
$$\begin{array}{r} 115 \\ \times\ 36 \\ \hline \end{array}$$

4
$$\begin{array}{r} 1{,}284 \\ \times \quad\ 4 \\ \hline \end{array}$$

5
$$\begin{array}{r} 2{,}394 \\ \times \quad\ 4 \\ \hline \end{array}$$

6 $60 \overline{)\,3600}$

7 $12 \overline{)\,1920}$

8 $36 \overline{)\,8820}$

READY TO GO Converting Measurements

Jessica needs 1 meter of blue fabric and 300 centimeters of green fabric. How many more meters of green fabric than blue fabric does Jessica need?

1 Convert 300 centimeters to its equivalent in meters.

- Centimeters are smaller than meters.

  1 meter = 100 centimeters

- Divide to convert centimeters to meters.

  centimeters ÷ 100 = meters

  300 ÷ 100 = 3

  300 centimeters = 3 meters

2 Subtract 1 meter from 3 meters.

3 − 1 = 2

To convert a smaller unit to a larger unit, I need to divide.

$$\begin{array}{r} 3 \\ 100\overline{)300} \\ -300 \\ \hline 0 \end{array}$$

Jessica needs 2 more meters of green fabric than blue fabric.

 DISCUSS Think of a real-life situation in which you might need to convert between different units of measure, and discuss it with your classmates.

LESSON LINK

PLUG IN	POWER UP	GO!
Within each system of measurement, you can compare equivalent quantities that use different units of measure.	You can multiply and divide multi-digit whole numbers.	I get it! I can use multiplication and division to find equivalent quantities when different units of measure are used in word problems.

PLUG IN

Within each system of measurement, you can compare equivalent quantities that use different units of measure.

Customary: 1 lb is 16 times heavier than 1 oz.

Metric: 1 kg is 1,000 times heavier than 1 g.

POWER UP

You can multiply and divide multi-digit whole numbers.

$$\begin{array}{r} {}^{2} \\ 205 \\ \times\quad 4 \\ \hline 820 \end{array}$$

$$\begin{array}{r} 5 \\ 36\overline{)180} \\ -180 \\ \hline 0 \end{array}$$

GO!

I get it! I can use multiplication and division to find equivalent quantities when different units of measure are used in word problems.

A conversion table shows the relationship between the units you are converting.

WORK TOGETHER

You can use a conversion table to help you solve a real-world problem.

- The conversion table shows the pattern between seconds and minutes.

- Find 240 seconds in the table.
240 seconds = 4 minutes

Gabrielle ran for 4 minutes.

Gabrielle ran for 240 seconds. For how many minutes did Gabrielle run?

Pattern: seconds ÷ 60 = minutes

Seconds	Minutes
60	1
120	2
180	3
240	**4**
300	5

Customary and Metric Units can be found on p. 249.

A You can use a conversion table to solve a problem.

DO

The distance from Oscar's house to school is 3 kilometers. What is the distance in meters?

1. Identify the pattern.
2. Complete the conversion table.
3. Find 3 kilometers in the table.
4. Answer the question.

Pattern: _____ × _____ = meters

Kilometers	Meters
1	**1,000**
2	
3	
4	

The distance from Oscar's house to school is _____ meters.

B You can write a conversion and use it to solve a problem.

DO

Riley drank 2,000 milliliters of water on Monday. How many liters of water did Riley drink on Monday?

1. Write a conversion that you can use to convert milliliters to liters.
2. Convert 2,000 milliliters to liters.
3. Fill in the answer.

_____ ÷ _____ = liters

_____ ÷ _____ = _____

Riley drank _____ liters of water on Monday.

Are quarts larger or smaller than pints?

DISCUSS

Benito wants to convert 4 quarts to pints by dividing 4 ÷ 2. What can you tell Benito?

PRACTICE

Customary and Metric Units can be found on p. 249.

Use Math Tool: Customary and Metric Units for problems 1–4.

Complete the conversion table. Then use it to solve the problem.

1 A cantaloupe weighs 48 ounces. How many pounds does the cantaloupe weigh?

Ounces	Pounds
16	1
32	
48	
60	
72	

Pattern: ____ounces____ ÷ _____ = pounds

_____ ÷ _____ = _____

The cantaloupe weighs _____ pounds.

2 Hunter's dog weighs 27 kilograms. How many grams does Hunter's dog weigh?

REMEMBER
To convert to a larger unit, divide.

Kilograms	Grams
1	
25	
26	
27	
28	

Pattern: _____ × _____ = grams

_____ × _____ = _____

Hunter's dog weighs _____ grams.

Write a conversion and use it to solve the problem.

3 A pitcher holds 3 liters of water. How many milliliters of water does the pitcher hold?

____liters____ × _____ = milliliters

_____ × _____ = _____

The pitcher holds _____ milliliters of water.

HINT
1 L = 1,000 mL

4 Matthew's football practice was 120 minutes long. How many hours long was Matthew's football practice?

_____ ÷ _____ = hours

_____ ÷ _____ = _____

Matthew's football practice

was _____ hours long.

Solve.

5 Faith spends 5 hours a week doing her homework. Audrey spends 180 minutes a week doing her homework. In one week, how many more minutes does Faith spend doing her homework than Audrey?

_____ × _____ = minutes

_____ × _____ = _____

5 hours = _____ minutes

_____ − _____ = _____

In one week, Faith spends _____ more minutes doing her homework than Audrey.

6 Isaiah buys 14 kilograms of green apples and 8,000 grams of red apples. How many more kilograms of green apples than red apples did Isaiah buy?

_____ ÷ _____ = kilograms

_____ ÷ _____ = _____

8,000 g = _____ kg

_____ − _____ = _____

Isaiah bought _____ more kilograms of green apples than red apples.

Solve.

I will look for words like "farther away" and "cuts off" that tell me which operation to use.

7 Carter lives 3 kilometers away from the school. Kyle lives 2,000 meters farther away from the school than Carter does. How many meters away from the school does Kyle live? _____

8 Sophie has a ribbon that is 5 yards long. She cuts off a 9-foot-long section. How many yards long is Sophie's ribbon now? _____

Divide to convert to a larger unit.

DISCUSS **Check the Reasoning**

Aaron is converting 2,000 grams to kilograms. He says he needs to multiply by 1,000. Is Aaron correct? Explain why or why not.

PROBLEM SOLVING

PEANUT BUTTER SANDWICHES

READ

Mrs. Hall opens a new 1-kilogram jar of peanut butter. She uses 120 grams to make sandwiches. How many grams of peanut butter does Mrs. Hall have left?

PLAN

• What is the problem asking you to find?

How many _____ of peanut butter Mrs. Hall has left

• What do you need to know to solve the problem?

The original amount of peanut butter in the jar: _____

The amount of peanut butter she used: _____

• How can you find the amount of peanut butter Mrs. Hall has left?

Convert the total amount of peanut butter in the jar to grams. Then subtract the amount of peanut butter used from the total amount of peanut butter.

SOLVE

Convert kilograms to grams.

_____ × _____ = grams

_____ × _____ = _____ g

Subtract to find how many grams of peanut butter Mrs. Hall has left.

_____ − _____ = _____ g

CHECK

Use addition.

amount used + amount left = original amount

_____ g + _____ g = _____ g

Convert grams to kilograms.

_____ ÷ _____ = kilograms

_____ ÷ _____ = _____ kg

1,000 grams = _____ kilogram

Mrs. Hall has _____ grams of peanut butter left.

> I get it! I can use inverse operation to check my answer.

PRACTICE

Use the problem-solving steps to help you.

Decide if you are converting to a larger unit or to a smaller unit.

1 Most people sleep an average of 8 hours per night. Pilar sleeps 600 minutes per night. How many more minutes than average does Pilar sleep?

CHECKLIST
- [ ] READ
- [ ] PLAN
- [ ] SOLVE
- [ ] CHECK

2 Ice Cream Delight uses 500 milliliters of milk in each milkshake. If the shop sells 4 milkshakes, how many liters of milk will it use?

CHECKLIST
- [ ] READ
- [ ] PLAN
- [ ] SOLVE
- [ ] CHECK

3 Landon has a 10-pound bag of flour. He spills 64 ounces of flour. How many pounds of flour does Landon have left?

CHECKLIST
- [ ] READ
- [ ] PLAN
- [ ] SOLVE
- [ ] CHECK

16 Line Plots

PLUG IN Creating Line Plots

A **line plot** is a way to show data using a number line. Each X on a line plot shows the number of times the value below it occurs in a set of data.

A botanist measured the growth of some plants during an experiment. Here are the results, in fractions of an inch.

$$\frac{1}{8}, \frac{3}{8}, \frac{3}{8}, \frac{2}{8}, \frac{7}{8}, \frac{4}{8}, \frac{6}{8}$$

You can display these measurements in a line plot.

> Numbers on a number line should be equally spaced.

To draw a line plot, first draw a number line. The number line should begin at or to the left of the least data value, $\frac{1}{8}$, and end at or to the right of the greatest data value, $\frac{7}{8}$.

Label each tic mark with a fraction that has a denominator of 8.

> Even though the value $\frac{5}{8}$ is not included in the data set, it is shown on the number line.

Draw an X above each number for each time it appears in the data set. Be sure to include a title for the line plot.

Plant Growth (in inches)

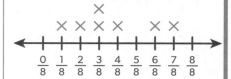

You can use a line plot to compare the frequencies of the values in the data set. The most common amount of growth among the plants was $\frac{3}{8}$ inch.

> Two plants had a growth of $\frac{3}{8}$ inch, so there are 2 Xs above $\frac{3}{8}$ on the number line.

Words to Know

line plot
a graph that uses Xs above a number line to display data

DISCUSS

Duncan drew a line plot to show data about the masses, in kilograms, of some kittens.

$$\frac{2}{10}, \frac{6}{10}, \frac{4}{10}, \frac{1}{10}, \frac{2}{10}, \frac{4}{10}, \frac{1}{10}$$

Masses of Kittens (in kilograms)

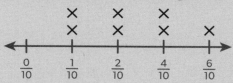

What can you tell Duncan about his line plot?

A You can create a line plot from a set of data.

DO

A track coach recorded the times it took his runners to react after the starting bell rang. The times, in fractions of a second, were $\frac{1}{6}, \frac{1}{6}, \frac{5}{6}, \frac{2}{6}, \frac{3}{6}, \frac{2}{6}$, and $\frac{1}{6}$. Display this data on a line plot.

1 Fill in the missing numbers on the number line.

2 Draw an X on the line plot for each data value.

3 Give the line plot a title.

$\frac{0}{6}$ $\frac{1}{6}$ $\frac{2}{6}$ $\frac{6}{6}$

B You can interpret the data in a line plot.

DO

The line plot shows the weights in pounds of the puppies in a litter. How many puppies weighed $\frac{7}{10}$ pound?

1 Find and circle $\frac{7}{10}$ on the number line.

2 Find the number of Xs above $\frac{7}{10}$.

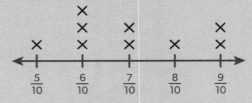

Puppy Weights (in pounds)

$\frac{5}{10}$ $\frac{6}{10}$ $\frac{7}{10}$ $\frac{8}{10}$ $\frac{9}{10}$

There are ___**2**___ Xs above $\frac{7}{10}$ on the number line.

So, _____ puppies in the litter weighed $\frac{7}{10}$ pound.

PRACTICE

Create a line plot to display the data. Include a title.

1 The times, in hours, that it took 8 students to clean their rooms: $\frac{3}{12}, \frac{6}{12}, \frac{4}{12}, \frac{4}{12}, \frac{2}{12}, \frac{3}{12}, \frac{6}{12}, \frac{6}{12}$.

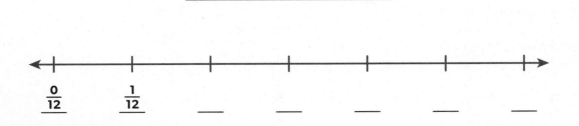

$\frac{0}{12}$ $\frac{1}{12}$

Operations with Fractions

To add or subtract fractions with like denominators, add or subtract the numerators and use the same denominator.

$$\frac{1}{5} + \frac{3}{5} = \frac{1+3}{5} = \frac{4}{5}$$

To add or subtract **mixed numbers** with like denominators, rename as improper fractions and subtract.

Subtract: $2\frac{5}{8} - 1\frac{2}{8}$

$$2\frac{5}{8} = \frac{(2 \times 8) + 5}{8} = \frac{21}{8}$$

$$1\frac{2}{8} = \frac{(1 \times 8) + 2}{8} = \frac{10}{8}$$

$$\frac{21}{8} - \frac{10}{8} = \frac{11}{8} = 1\frac{3}{8}$$

$$2\frac{5}{8} - 1\frac{2}{8} = 1\frac{3}{8}$$

To multiply a whole number by a fraction, write the whole number as a fraction with a denominator of 1. Then multiply the numerators and multiply the denominators.

$$\frac{1}{4} \times 5 = \frac{1}{4} \times \frac{5}{1}$$
$$= \frac{1 \times 5}{4 \times 1}$$
$$= \frac{5}{4}$$

 I see! The denominator stays the same when you multiply a fraction by a whole number because the denominator of a whole number is 1.

To multiply a whole number by a mixed number, write the mixed number as an **improper fraction**. Write the whole number as a fraction with a denominator of 1.

Multiply: $1\frac{1}{4} \times 3$

$$1\frac{1}{4} = \frac{(1 \times 4) + 1}{4} = \frac{5}{4}$$
$$3 = \frac{3}{1}$$

Multiply the numerators and multiply the denominators.

$$\frac{5}{4} \times \frac{3}{1} = \frac{5 \times 3}{4 \times 1} = \frac{15}{4}$$

I can rename the product as a mixed number. $\frac{15}{4}$ is equivalent to $3\frac{3}{4}$.

Words to Know

mixed number
a number with a whole-number part and a fraction part

improper fraction
a fraction with a numerator that is greater than or equal to the denominator

 DISCUSS Describe how you would find the sum of $1\frac{1}{5}$ and $2\frac{3}{5}$.

A You can subtract fractions and mixed numbers.

DO Subtract: $5\frac{4}{7} - \frac{6}{7}$

❶ Rename the mixed number as an improper fraction.

❷ Subtract the fractions.

❸ Rename the difference as a mixed number.

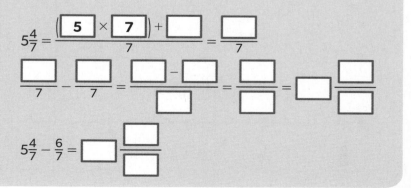

$$5\frac{4}{7} = \frac{(\boxed{5} \times \boxed{7}) + \boxed{}}{7} = \frac{\boxed{}}{7}$$

$$\frac{\boxed{}}{7} - \frac{\boxed{}}{7} = \frac{\boxed{} - \boxed{}}{\boxed{}} = \frac{\boxed{}}{\boxed{}} = \boxed{}\frac{\boxed{}}{\boxed{}}$$

$$5\frac{4}{7} - \frac{6}{7} = \boxed{}\frac{\boxed{}}{\boxed{}}$$

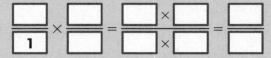
Any whole number can be written as a fraction.

B You can multiply a whole number by a fraction.

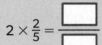
Multiply: $2 \times \frac{2}{5}$

1 Write the whole number as a fraction with a denominator of 1.

2 Multiply the numerators and multiply the denominators.

3 Write the product.

$$\frac{\boxed{}}{\boxed{1}} \times \frac{\boxed{}}{\boxed{}} = \frac{\boxed{} \times \boxed{}}{\boxed{} \times \boxed{}} = \frac{\boxed{}}{\boxed{}}$$

$$2 \times \frac{2}{5} = \frac{\boxed{}}{\boxed{}}$$

C You can multiply a whole number by a mixed number.

Multiply: $4 \times 2\frac{1}{6}$

1 Rename the mixed number as an improper fraction.

2 Write the whole number as a fraction with a denominator of 1.

3 Multiply the numerators and multiply the denominators.

4 Write the product as a mixed number.

$$2\frac{1}{6} = \frac{(\boxed{} \times \boxed{}) + \boxed{}}{\boxed{6}} = \frac{\boxed{}}{\boxed{}}$$

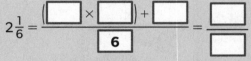

$$\frac{\boxed{}}{\boxed{}} \times \frac{\boxed{}}{\boxed{}} = \frac{\boxed{} \times \boxed{}}{\boxed{} \times \boxed{}} = \frac{\boxed{}}{\boxed{}} = \boxed{} \frac{\boxed{}}{\boxed{}}$$

$$4 \times 2\frac{1}{6} = \boxed{} \frac{\boxed{}}{\boxed{}}$$

DISCUSS Rocco says that the sum of $\frac{3}{7}$ and $\frac{2}{7}$ is $\frac{5}{14}$. Is he correct? Explain.

PRACTICE

Add or subtract.

1 $\frac{1}{7} + \frac{4}{7} = \frac{\boxed{5}}{\boxed{}}$

2 $\frac{8}{9} - \frac{1}{9} = \frac{\boxed{}}{\boxed{}}$

3 $2\frac{2}{3} + 3\frac{2}{3} = \boxed{} \frac{\boxed{}}{\boxed{}}$

4 $5\frac{2}{6} - 1\frac{3}{6} = \boxed{} \frac{\boxed{}}{\boxed{}}$

Multiply.

5 $5 \times \frac{3}{7} = \frac{\boxed{}}{\boxed{}} = \boxed{} \frac{\boxed{}}{\boxed{}}$

6 $4 \times \frac{2}{9} = \frac{\boxed{}}{\boxed{}}$

You can use the data in a line plot to solve a problem or answer a question.

This line plot shows the weights of several apples.

Apple Weights (in pounds)

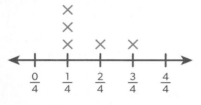

$$\frac{0}{4} \quad \frac{1}{4} \quad \frac{2}{4} \quad \frac{3}{4} \quad \frac{4}{4}$$

> I remember! The number of Xs over a value tells me how many times that value appears in the data set.

Find the total weight of all of the apples.

Find the number of Xs above each number.

There are 3 Xs above $\frac{1}{4}$.

There is 1 X above $\frac{2}{4}$.

There is 1 X above $\frac{3}{4}$.

> Each X stands for a number in the data set.

Write an addition sentence to find the sum of the weights of all of the apples.

$$\frac{1}{4} + \frac{1}{4} + \frac{1}{4} + \frac{2}{4} + \frac{3}{4}$$

$$\frac{1 + 1 + 1 + 2 + 3}{4} = \frac{8}{4}$$

The fraction $\frac{8}{4}$ is the same as $8 \div 4$, or 2. The total weight of the apples is 2 pounds.

> To add fractions with the same denominator, I add the numerators and use the same denominator.

DISCUSS In the line plot above, there are 3 Xs over the number $\frac{1}{4}$. How could you find the total weight of the apples that weigh $\frac{1}{4}$ pound? Can you think of more than one way? What is the total weight?

LESSON LINK

PLUG IN

You can create and read a line plot that displays a set of data.

Juice (in cups)

$$0 \quad \frac{1}{4} \quad \frac{2}{4} \quad \frac{3}{4} \quad 1$$

POWER UP

You can add, subtract, and multiply fractions, mixed numbers, and whole numbers.

$$\frac{2}{5} + 3\frac{1}{5} = 3\frac{3}{5}$$

$$\frac{7}{8} - \frac{4}{8} = \frac{3}{8}$$

$$3 \times \frac{3}{4} = \frac{9}{4} = 2\frac{1}{4}$$

$$8 \times 1\frac{1}{4} = \frac{40}{4} = 10$$

GO!

> I get it! I can use the data from a line plot and what I know about fractions to solve problems involving line plots.

WORK TOGETHER

You can solve a problem using the data in a line plot.

- Use multiplication and addition to find the total amount of paint.

- Divide the total amount by 5 to find the amount in each can.

There will be 1 gallon of paint in each can.

The line plot shows the amount of paint left in some paint cans. If all of the paint is poured equally into 5 cans, how much paint will be in each can?

Paint Left in Paint Cans (in gallons)

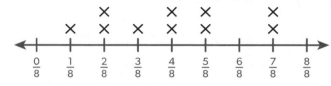

$$\left(1 \times \frac{1}{8}\right) + \left(2 \times \frac{2}{8}\right) + \left(1 \times \frac{3}{8}\right) + \left(2 \times \frac{4}{8}\right) + \left(2 \times \frac{5}{8}\right) + \left(2 \times \frac{7}{8}\right)$$

$$\left(\frac{1}{1} \times \frac{1}{8}\right) + \left(\frac{2}{1} \times \frac{2}{8}\right) + \left(\frac{1}{1} \times \frac{3}{8}\right) + \left(\frac{2}{1} \times \frac{4}{8}\right) + \left(\frac{2}{1} \times \frac{5}{8}\right) + \left(\frac{2}{1} \times \frac{7}{8}\right)$$

$$= \frac{1}{8} + \frac{4}{8} + \frac{3}{8} + \frac{8}{8} + \frac{10}{8} + \frac{14}{8}$$

$$= \frac{40}{8} = 5$$

5 gallons ÷ 5 = 1 gallon

A You can solve a problem using data from a line plot.

DO

The line plot shows the lengths of leaves on a plant. If the leaves were laid end-to-end along a line, how long would the line be?

Leaf Lengths (in inches)

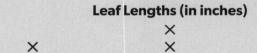

1 Find the number of Xs above each number.

2 Multiply and add to find the total length.

$$\left(2 \times \frac{1}{6}\right) + \left(\underline{\hspace{1cm}} \times \frac{2}{6}\right) + \left(\underline{\hspace{1cm}} \times \frac{3}{6}\right) + \left(\underline{\hspace{1cm}} \times \frac{4}{6}\right)$$

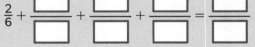

$$\frac{2}{6} + \frac{\boxed{}}{\boxed{}} + \frac{\boxed{}}{\boxed{}} + \frac{\boxed{}}{\boxed{}} = \frac{\boxed{}}{\boxed{}}$$

The line would be $\frac{\boxed{}}{\boxed{}}$, or $\boxed{}\frac{\boxed{}}{\boxed{}}$ inches long.

DISCUSS How do you know whether to add, subtract, multiply, or divide to solve a problem?

PRACTICE

Use the line plot for problems 1 and 2. Show your work.

The line plot shows the amount of soda left in glasses after a party.

Soda Left (in cups)

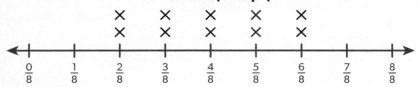

1 How much soda would be in each glass if the total amount in all of the glasses were redistributed equally?

$$\left(\underline{\hspace{1cm}} \times \frac{2}{8}\right) + \left(\underline{\hspace{1cm}} \times \frac{3}{8}\right) + \left(\underline{\hspace{1cm}} \times \frac{4}{8}\right) + \left(\underline{\hspace{1cm}} \times \frac{5}{8}\right) + \left(\underline{\hspace{1cm}} \times \frac{6}{8}\right) =$$

_____ cup

2 Yasmin pours out the four glasses with the least amount of soda in them. How much soda is left in the six remaining glasses?

_____ cups

Use the line plot for problem 3.

The line plot shows the weights of several shopping bags.

Shopping Bag Weights (in pounds)

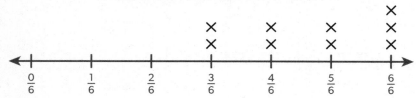

3 If the contents of the bags are redistributed so that the bags have equal weights, how much will each bag weigh?

_____ pound

Use the line plot for problem 4.

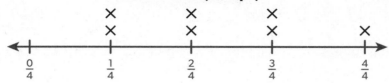

Butter Used (in cups)

4 Ginny made a line plot to show the amounts of butter used in some of the recipes at her family's Thanksgiving meal. How much butter was used to cook the meal?

$\dfrac{\boxed{}}{\boxed{}}$, or _____ cups

Use the line plot for problems 5–6.

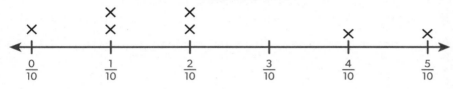

Rainfall (in inches)

I get it! Each X above a number represents one day with that amount of rainfall.

5 All of the days with $\frac{1}{10}$ inch rainfall occurred in the same week. What was the total rainfall for those days? _____

6 All of the days with $\frac{2}{10}$ inch rainfall were during the same storm. What was the total rainfall for those days? _____

Interpret Data

The line plot below shows how much time Lilah spent each day last week practicing piano.

Piano Practice Time (in hours)

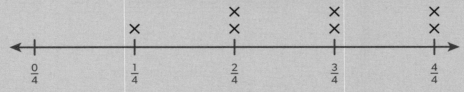

How can she find the total amount of time spent practicing last week?

How much time did Lilah spend practicing piano last week?

PROBLEM SOLVING

SEW WHAT?

READ

Nicole has some scraps of ribbon. The lengths of the scraps are displayed on the line plot.

She will make a new ribbon by sewing together the scraps that are at least $\frac{6}{8}$ inch long. How long will the new ribbon be?

Lengths of Scraps (in inches)

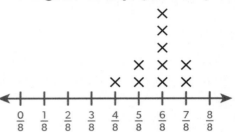

PLAN

• What is the problem asking you to find?

The _____ of the lengths of the scraps that are at least _____ inch long

• What do you need to do to solve this problem?

You need to add the data values that are greater than or equal to $\frac{6}{8}$.

SOLVE

There are _____ values on the line plot that are greater than or equal to _____.

Add the values:

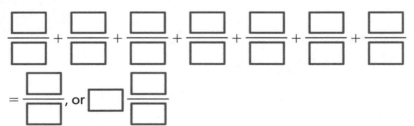

CHECK

To check your addition, use repeated subtraction.

Start with your answer, and subtract your seven addends. The difference should be 0.

The new ribbon will be ⬚/⬚ , or ⬚ ⬚/⬚ inches long.

PRACTICE

The sum of fractions with like denominators will have the same denominator.

Use the problem-solving steps to help you. Show your work.

1 The line plot below shows the lengths of pieces of fence. Jason will use the pieces that are longer than $\frac{4}{10}$ meter. What is the total length of the fence pieces that are longer than $\frac{4}{10}$ meter?

Lengths of Fence Pieces (in meters)

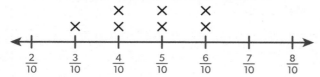

CHECKLIST
- [ ] READ
- [ ] PLAN
- [ ] SOLVE
- [ ] CHECK

2 The line plot below shows the amount of cooking oil in several bottles. Carrie will combine all of the oil from those bottles with at least $\frac{2}{6}$ cup left. How much oil will she have?

Amount of Cooking Oil (in cups)

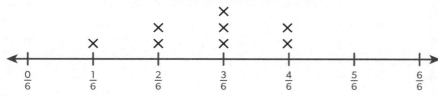

CHECKLIST
- [ ] READ
- [ ] PLAN
- [ ] SOLVE
- [ ] CHECK

3 The line plot below shows the weights of hacky sacks. To be used in a tournament, a hacky sack must weigh less than $\frac{3}{20}$ pound. Keira puts the hacky sacks for the tournament into a bag. What is the total weight of the hacky sacks in the bag?

Hacky Sack Weights (in pounds)

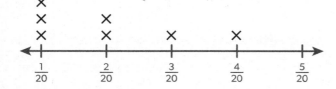

CHECKLIST
- [ ] READ
- [ ] PLAN
- [ ] SOLVE
- [ ] CHECK

17 Measuring Volume of Rectangular Prisms

PLUG IN Understanding Cubic Units

Volume is the measure of the amount of space inside a solid figure.

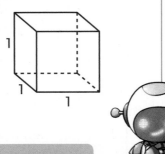

Volume is measured in **cubic units**. A **unit cube** is a cube with a side length of one unit and has a volume of one cubic unit.

1 unit
1 unit
1 unit

An inch cube has side lengths of one inch.

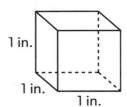

1 in.
1 in.
1 in.

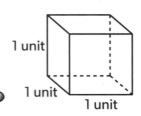

> I remember! A cube is a solid figure.

> A solid figure filled with one unit cube has a volume of one cubic unit.

> I know! The inch cube has a volume of one cubic inch.

Words to Know

volume	**unit cube**	**cubic unit**
the number of cubic units needed to fill a solid figure	a cube with a side length of 1 unit	a unit used to measure volume

DISCUSS Name an object whose area you can find, then name an object whose volume you can find. Explain the difference.

A You can measure volume in any cubic unit.

DO Find the volume of the cube.

1 Find the units used to show the length of each side of the cube.

2 Express the length of each side of the cube in the units given.

3 Determine the volume of the cube.

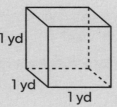

1 yd
1 yd
1 yd

Each side of the cube is measured in _____**yards**_____.

The length of each side of the cube is _____ yard.

The volume of the cube is _____.

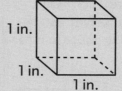

I see! The cube with the shorter side lengths has the lesser volume.

B You can find and compare the volumes of unit cubes.

DO Compare the volumes of the two cubes.

❶ Find the measure of each side of each cube.

❷ Find the volume of each cube. Use the appropriate cubic units.

❸ Compare the side lengths of the cubes.

❹ Compare the volumes of the cubes.

The cube on the left has a side length of __**1 cm**__.

The cube on the right has a side length of _____.

The volume of the cube on the left is

_____.

The volume of the cube on the right is _____

The length of 1 centimeter is _____ than 1 inch.

The volume of the cube on the left is _____ than the volume of the cube on the right.

PRACTICE

Find the volume of the unit cube.

1

1 mm
1 mm
1 mm

_____**1 cubic millimeter**_____

2

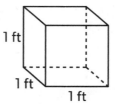

1 ft
1 ft
1 ft

_____

Find and compare the volumes of the unit cubes.

3

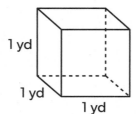

1 yd
1 yd
1 yd

1 m
1 m
1 m

The volume of the cube on the left is _____.

The volume of the cube on the right is _____.

The volume of the cube on the right is _____ than the volume of the cube on the left.

POWER UP | Understanding Volume

A solid figure, such as a **rectangular prism**, can be filled with unit cubes to measure its **volume**.

The unit cubes must be placed so that the **faces** touch, without spaces between them or overlaps.

The volume of the rectangular prism is equal to the number of unit cubes that fit inside of it.

Let's see how many cubes will fit inside the solid figure!

I see! The cubes are arranged in rows within the solid figure.

There are 15 cubes in each layer. There are 2 layers. The volume is 30 cubic units!

Words to Know

volume
the number of cubic units needed to fill a solid figure

faces
the flat surfaces of a solid figure

face

rectangular prism
a solid figure with faces that are rectangles

DISCUSS When finding the volume of a solid, why is it important that the unit cubes do not have gaps between them or overlap?

A You can count and add unit cubes to find the volume of a solid.

DO Find the volume of the figure.

① Count the unit cubes in one row.

② Count the number of rows.

③ Count the number of layers.

④ Add the number of cubes in each layer to find the volume.

There are ___**3**___ cubes in one row.

There are _____ rows.

There are _____ layers.

One layer: ___**21**___ cubes

Three layers: _____ + _____ + _____ = _____

The volume is _____ cubic units.

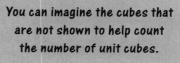 You can imagine the cubes that are not shown to help count the number of unit cubes.

B You can count and add unit cubes to find the volume.

DO  Find the volume of the figure.

1 Count the unit cubes in one row.

2 Count the number of rows.

3 Count the number of layers.

4 Add the number of cubes in each layer to find the volume.

There are ___3___ cubes in one row.

There are _____ rows.

There are _____ layers.

One layer: _____ cubes

Two layers: _____ + _____ = _____

The volume is _____ cubic units.

DISCUSS Peyton said that the volume of this solid is 16 cubic units. What can you tell Peyton about his work?

PRACTICE

Find the volume by counting the number of unit cubes that would fill the solid.

1

There are ___4___ cubes in one row.

There are _____ rows.

There are _____ layers.

One layer: ___20___ cubes

Four layers: ___20___ + _____ + _____ + _____ = _____

The volume is _____ cubic units.

2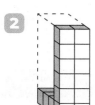

One layer: _____ cubes

There are _____ layers.

Four layers: _____ + _____ + _____ + _____ = _____

The volume is _____ cubic units.

Measuring Volume of Rectangular Prisms

The length of each side of a unit cube can be measured in different units, such as centimeters, inches, and feet.

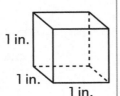

1 cm
1 cm 1 cm

1 in.
1 in. 1 in.

Cubic centimeters, **cubic inches**, and **cubic feet** can be used to measure the volume of a rectangular prism.

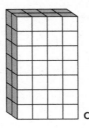

1 cubic centimeter

Each unit is 1 cubic centimeter.

Different unit cubes can be counted to find volume. Use the correct label after you count the unit cubes.

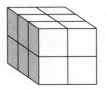

1 cubic inch

Each unit is 1 cubic inch.

Any unit of measure can be used to make a cubic unit!

There are 56 cubic centimeters in this rectangular prism.

I get it! The volume of this rectangular prism is 12 cubic inches.

Words to Know

cubic centimeter
a unit cube used to measure volume with a side length of 1 centimeter

cubic inch
a unit cube used to measure volume with a side length of 1 inch

cubic foot
a unit cube used to measure volume with a side length of 1 foot

DISCUSS What other units of measurement can be used to find volume? Give examples of objects and the units used to measure their volume.

LESSON LINK

PLUG IN ▶ **POWER UP** ▶ **GO!**

Unit cubes have one cubic unit of volume.

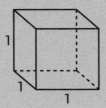

1
1
1

Volume is the number of unit cubes that fit inside a solid.

I understand! I can find the volume of a rectangular prism with side lengths that are measured in any unit used to measure length!

WORK TOGETHER

You can count and add unit cubes to find the volume.

- There are 9 cubes in each layer.

- There are 4 layers.

- Add 9 four times.

- Each unit cube is 1 cubic inch.

The volume of the prism is 36 cubic inches.

Find the volume of the rectangular prism in cubic inches.

1 cubic inch

$9 + 9 + 9 + 9 = 36$

In each layer, find the number of cubes in each row and the number of rows to find the total number of cubes in a layer.

A You can count and add unit cubes to find the volume.

DO Find the volume of this prism.

1. Count the number of cubes in each layer.

2. Count the number of layers.

3. Add to find the volume. Write the correct units.

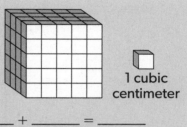
1 cubic centimeter

There are _____ cubes in each layer.

There are _____ layers.

_____ + _____ + _____ + _____ = _____

Each unit cube is 1 _____.

The volume of the prism is _____.

B You can count and add unit cubes to find the volume.

DO Find the volume of this prism.

1. Count the number of cubes in each layer.

2. Count the number of layers.

3. Add to find the volume. Write the correct units.

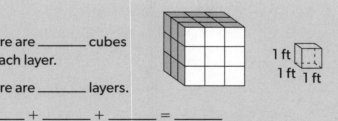
1 ft
1 ft 1 ft

There are _____ cubes in each layer.

There are _____ layers.

_____ + _____ + _____ = _____

Each unit cube is 1 _____.

The volume of the prism is _____.

DISCUSS Sharee does not know which units were used to measure the volume of a prism. She decides to write the volume in cubic centimeters. What could you tell Sharee?

Remember that not all cubic units are the same size!

PRACTICE

Find the volume of the rectangular prism. Label the volume with the correct units.

1 Each unit cube is 1 _____**cubic centimeter**_____.

There are _____ cubes in each layer.

There are _____ layers.

_____ + _____ + _____ = _____

The volume of the prism is _____ cubic centimeters.

2 Each unit cube is 1 _____.

There are _____ cubes in each layer.

There are _____ layers.

_____ + _____ = _____

The volume of the prism is _____.

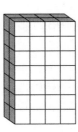

1 in.
1 in.
1 in.

3 Each unit cube is 1 _____.

___**40**___ + _____ = _____

The volume of the prism is _____.

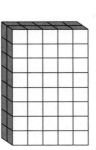

1 ft
1 ft
1 ft

4 Each unit cube is 1 _____.

The volume of the prism is _____.

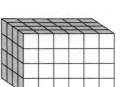

1 m
1 m
1 m

5 Each unit cube is 1 _____.

The volume of the prism is _____.

1 cm
1 cm
1 cm

Find the volumes. Label the volumes with the correct units.

6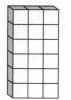

1 in.
1 in. 1 in.

The volume is _____.

7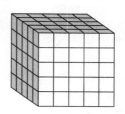

1 ft
1 ft 1 ft

The volume is _____.

Find the volumes.

8 Brad fills a fish tank shaped like a rectangular prism with 1-inch cubes. Each layer has 4 rows, with 3 cubes in each row. He can fit 3 layers of cubes in the tank. What is the volume?

_____

9 Joyce fills a small box with 1-centimeter cubes. She can fit 4 layers of cubes in the box. Each layer has 3 rows, with 9 cubes in each row. What is the volume of the box?

_____

Remember to write the correct units!

DISCUSS

Make Sense of a Problem

Ciara built a solid figure with 1-inch cubes. Her figure had 3 layers, with 2 rows of 6 cubes in each layer. She built a second solid figure with 4 layers. This figure had 3 rows, with 3 cubes in each row. Are the volumes of the figures the same?

What is the volume of the first figure?

What is the volume of the second figure?

How do the volumes compare?

PROBLEM SOLVING

STORING BLOCKS

READ

Felix built a crate to hold 1-inch cube blocks. The volume of the crate is 64 cubic inches. Is it large enough to hold 4 layers of blocks, with 3 rows of 5 blocks in each row?

PLAN

• What is the problem asking you to find?

   The _____ of the blocks

• What do you need to know to solve this problem?

   You need to know the number of rows, blocks, and layers.

   There are _____ layers, with _____ rows and _____ blocks in each row.

• How can you find the volume of the blocks?

   Count the number of blocks in each _____.

   Add to find the _____ number of blocks.

SOLVE

Find the volume of the blocks.

Determine the number of blocks in one layer. _____

Add to find the number of blocks in four layers.

_____ + _____ + _____ + _____ = _____

CHECK

Use a model to find the volume.

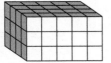

Count the number of blocks in one layer. _____

Add to find the number of blocks in four layers.

_____ + _____ + _____ + _____ = _____

Will all of the blocks fit inside Felix's crate? _____

PRACTICE

Use the problem-solving steps to help you.

Find the volume of the first solid figure first.

1 Alison built a solid figure using centimeter cubes. She built 6 layers, with each layer having 4 rows of 2 blocks. She wants to build another solid figure, with the same volume, that has 3 rows of 8 cubes in each layer. How many layers are in the new solid figure?

CHECKLIST
☐ READ
☐ PLAN
☐ SOLVE
☐ CHECK

2 A cabinet was filled with 4 layers of 1-foot cubes. Each layer has 4 rows, with 4 cubes in each row. What is valume of the cabinet?

CHECKLIST
☐ READ
☐ PLAN
☐ SOLVE
☐ CHECK

3 A trunk has a volume of 75 cubic feet. If the trunk can be filled with 5 layers of 1-foot cubes, with 3 equal rows in each layer, how many cubes are in each row?

CHECKLIST
☐ READ
☐ PLAN
☐ SOLVE
☐ CHECK

Formulas for Volume of Rectangular Prisms

PLUG IN — Using the Formula for Area of a Rectangle

The **area** (*A*) of a rectangle is the number of 1-unit squares needed to cover it with no gaps or overlaps.

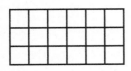

☐ = 1 square unit

You can use a **formula** to find the area of a rectangle.

3 inches

6 inches

Area = length × width

$A = l \times w$

Area is measured in **square units**. Substitute the given values into the formula.

$A = l \times w$

$A = 6 \times 3$

$A = 18$ square inches

There are 18 square units covering this rectangle.

The length of this rectangle is 6 inches. The width is 3 inches.

The area is in square inches because we are measuring area using a unit that is 1 square inch.

Words to Know

area
the number of unit squares needed to cover a flat figure with no gaps or overlaps

formula
a special type of equation that shows a mathematical relationship

square unit
a square with a side length of 1 unit, used to measure the area of a flat figure

DISCUSS Willa drew a rectangle 9 centimeters long and 6 centimeters wide. Keisha drew a rectangle 8 centimeters long and 7 centimeters wide. Whose rectangle has the greater area?

A You can use a formula to find the area of a rectangle.

DO Find the area of the rectangle.

❶ Write the formula for the area of a rectangle.

❷ Substitute the given values into the formula.

❸ Multiply.

12 in.

3 in.

$A = \underline{\quad l \quad} \times \underline{\quad w \quad}$

$A = \underline{\qquad} \times \underline{\qquad} = \underline{\qquad}$

The area of the rectangle is _____ square inches.

B You can use the area formula to find a missing measure.

DO Find the missing measure.

1. Write the formula for the area of a rectangle.

2. Substitute the given values into the formula.

3. Divide to solve for w.

4. Check by multiplying.

To check, I can multiply the length by the width I calculated. The product should be the area!

5 m

w | $A = 20$ sq. m

$A =$ _____ × _____

_____**20**_____ = _____ × w

$w =$ _____ ÷ _____ = _____

Check: _____ × _____ = _____

The width of the rectangle is _____ meters.

PRACTICE

Find the area of the rectangle.

1

10 ft

6 ft

$A =$ ___**l**___ × _____

$A =$ _____ × _____ = _____

The area is _____ square feet.

2

15 cm

8 cm

$A =$ _____ × _____ = _____

The area is _____ square centimeters.

Find the missing measure.

3

l

4 in. | $A = 32$ sq. in.

$A =$ _____ × _____

$32 =$ _____ × _____

$l = 32 ÷$ _____ = _____

The length is _____ inches.

4

6 m

w | $A = 42$ sq. m

$A =$ _____ × _____

_____ = _____ × _____

$w =$ _____ ÷ _____ = _____

The width is _____ meters.

Measuring Volume of Rectangular Prisms

The **volume** of a solid figure is the measure of the number of unit cubes needed to fill it.

To find the volume of a **rectangular prism**, count the number of unit cubes in the **base** layer.

The other layers have the same number of cubes as the base layer.

You can also multiply the number of cubes in the base by the number of layers.

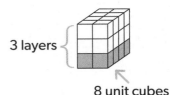

3 layers

8 unit cubes

$8 \times 3 = 24$ cubic units

I remember! Volume is measured in cubic units. Each unit cube has a volume of one cubic unit.

There are 3 layers of 8 cubes. Since $8 + 8 + 8 = 24$, then the volume is 24 cubic units.

I get it! This is the same as multiplying the area of the base by the height of the prism!

Words to Know

volume
the number of unit cubes needed to fill a solid figure

rectangular prism
a solid figure with faces that are rectangles

base
any face of a rectangular prism

DISCUSS Why does counting the unit cubes in a rectangular prism result in the same volume as multiplying the number of cubes in the base by the number of layers? Does it make a difference which method is used?

A You can count the unit cubes to find the volume of a prism.

DO Find the volume of the prism.

1 Count the number of cubes in a base layer.

2 Count the number of layers.

3 Multiply the number of cubes in the base layer by the number of layers.

4 Write the volume.

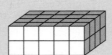

There are ____**20**____ cubes in the base layer.

There are _____ layers.

Multiply: _____ × _____ = _____

The volume of the prism is _____ cubic units.

B You can multiply the area of the base by the height to find the volume.

Find the area of the base by multiplying the length × width.

DO

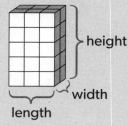

height

width

length

1 Determine the length, width, and height of the prism.

2 Find the area of the base.

3 Multiply the area of the base by the height.

The length is ___3___ unit cubes.

The width is _____ unit cubes.

The height is _____ unit cubes.

Multiply the length by the width.

_____ × _____ = _____ square units

Multiply the area of the base by the height to find the volume.

_____ × _____ = _____

The volume of the prism is _____ cubic units.

DISCUSS

Rayna and Micah are finding the volume of the same prism.

Rayna says the area of the base is 8 × 2 = 16. Micah says the area of the base is 2 × 3 = 6. Can both accurately find the volume of the cube? Explain.

PRACTICE

Find the volume.

1

Multiply the length by the width to find the area of the base.

_____ × _____ = _____ square units

Multiply the area of the base by the height to find the volume.

_____ × _____ = _____

The volume of the prism is _____ cubic units.

2

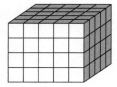

The volume of the prism is _____ cubic units.

READY TO GO | Formulas for Volume of Rectangular Prisms

Use a formula to find the volume of the rectangular prism.

1 Determine the length, width, and height.

2 Use the formula $V = l \times w \times h$, where l is the length, w is the width, and h is the height of the prism.

$$V = 6 \times 3 \times 5 = 90$$

3 Or, use the formula $V = B \times h$, where B is the area of the base and h is the height.

$$V = 18 \times 5 = 90$$

The volume of the prism is 90 cubic centimeters.

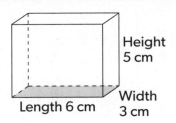

Height 5 cm
Length 6 cm
Width 3 cm

$6 \text{ cm} \times 3 \text{ cm} = 18 \text{ sq cm}$

The area of the base is 18 square centimeters.

> I get it! Since $B = l \times w$, both formulas multiply length, width, and height to find the volume.

DISCUSS Which dimensions are used to identify the area of the base layer in the formula $V = B \times h$? How is this helpful?

LESSON LINK

PLUG IN

You can find the area of a rectangle by multiplying its length and width.

9 in.
5 in.

$A = l \times w$

$A = 9 \times 5$

$A = 45$ square inches

POWER UP

You can find the volume of a rectangular prism by counting the number of unit cubes.

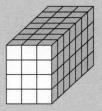

There are 21 cubes in the bottom layer. There are 4 layers.

$V = 21 \times 4 = 84$ cubic units

GO!

> I can find the volume of a rectangular prism by multiplying its length, width, and height, or by multiplying the area of its base by the height!

WORK TOGETHER

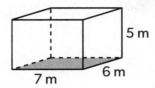

Multiply 7 and 6 first, then multiply that product and 5 to find the volume.

Use formulas to find the volume of the rectangular prism.

- The length is 7 meters.
  The width is 6 meters.
  The height is 5 meters.

- Substitute 7, 6, and 5 into the formula $V = l \times w \times h$. Multiply.

The volume is 210 cubic meters.

5 m

7 m   6 m

$V = l \times w \times h$

$V = 7 \times 6 \times 5$

$V = 210$ cubic meters

A You can use the formula $V = l \times w \times h$ to find the volume of a rectangular prism.

DO Find the volume of the prism.

1. Substitute the values into the formula.

2. Multiply.

3 in.

6 in.   4 in.

$V = l \times w \times h$

$V = \underline{\hspace{1cm}} \times \underline{\hspace{1cm}} \times \underline{\hspace{1cm}} = \underline{\hspace{1cm}}$

The volume of the prism is \underline{\hspace{1cm}} cubic inches.

B You can use the formula $V = B \times h$ to find the volume of a rectangular prism.

DO Find the volume of the prism.

1. Determine the base area and the height.

2. Substitute the values into the formula.

3. Multiply.

2 cm

24 sq cm

$V = B \times h$

$V = \underline{\hspace{1cm}} \times \underline{\hspace{1cm}} = \underline{\hspace{1cm}}$

The volume of the prism is \underline{\hspace{1cm}} cubic centimeters.

DISCUSS Christina says that the volume of a cube with a side length of 5 feet is 25 cubic feet. What can you tell Christina about her work?

179

PRACTICE

Find the volume of the rectangular prism.

1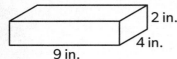
2 in.
4 in.
9 in.

$V = l \times w \times h$

$V = \underline{\quad 9 \quad} \times \underline{\qquad} \times \underline{\qquad}$

$V = \underline{\qquad}$

The volume is _____ cubic inches.

2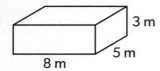
3 m
5 m
8 m

$V = l \times w \times h$

$V = \underline{\qquad} \times \underline{\qquad} \times \underline{\qquad}$

$V = \underline{\qquad}$

The volume is _____ cubic meters.

3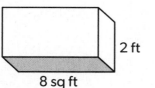
2 ft
8 sq ft

$V = B \times h$

$V = \underline{\qquad} \times \underline{\qquad}$

$V = \underline{\qquad}$

The volume is _____ cubic feet.

Find the volume of the rectangular prism.

4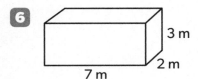

5 cm

20 sq cm

The volume is _____ cubic centimeters.

5

4 in.

16 sq in.

The volume is _____ cubic inches.

6

3 m

2 m

7 m

The volume is _____ cubic meters.

Solve. Include the units in your answer.

7 A cereal box is 8 inches long, 3 inches wide, and 10 inches high. What is the volume of the cereal box?

_____

8 A room has a floor area of 120 square feet and a height of 8 feet. What is the volume of the room?

_____

I get it! If I am given the length, width, and height, I can use $V = l \times w \times h$. If I am given the base area, I can use $V = B \times h$.

DISCUSS

See the Relationship

I remember! I can use division to find a missing measure.

Jon wants to find the height of a gift box. He knows the volume of the box is 90 cubic inches and the base area is 10 square inches.

How can he find the height of the box?

What is the height of the box?

PROBLEM SOLVING

TAKING A DIP

READ

Shane's wading pool is 4 feet long, 3 feet wide, and 2 feet high. Gwen's wading pool is 2 feet high with a base area of 10 square feet. Whose pool has the greater volume?

PLAN

• What is the problem asking you to find?

The _____ of each pool

The pool that has the greater _____

• What do you need to know to solve this problem?

You need to know the length, width, and height of Shane's pool.

length: _____ feet   width: _____ feet   height: _____ feet

You need to know the base area and height of Gwen's pool.

base area: _____ square feet   height _____ feet

• How can you find the volume?

You can use the formulas for the volume of a rectangular prism.

$V =$ _____ $\times$ _____ $\times$ _____ and $V =$ _____ $\times$ _____

SOLVE

Substitute the values into the formula for Shane's pool. Then multiply.

$V =$ _____ $\times$ _____ $\times$ _____

$V =$ _____ cubic feet

Substitute the values into the formula for Gwen's pool. Then multiply.

$V =$ _____ $\times$ _____

$V =$ _____ cubic feet

CHECK

The two pools have the same height, 2 feet. So, the pool with the greater base area will have the greater volume.

The base area of Gwen's pool is _____ square feet.

The base area of Shane's pool is _____ $\times$ _____ $=$ _____ square feet.

_____ pool has the greater volume.

I know! The base area is equal to length × width.

PRACTICE

Use the problem-solving steps to help you.

1 Brooke built a planter box that was 5 feet long, 4 feet wide, and 3 feet high. Megan built a planter box that was 3 feet high with a base area of 22 square feet. Whose planter box holds more soil?

CHECKLIST
- [ ] READ
- [ ] PLAN
- [ ] SOLVE
- [ ] CHECK

2 Mark and Kevin are packing books for a move. Mark's box is in the shape of a cube with an edge length of 2 feet. Kevin's box is 2 feet high with a base area of 5 square feet. Whose box holds more books?

CHECKLIST
- [ ] READ
- [ ] PLAN
- [ ] SOLVE
- [ ] CHECK

3 Cameron's fish tank is 20 inches long, 15 inches wide, and 12 inches high. Roberto's fish tank is 12 inches high with a base area of 250 square inches. Whose tank holds more water?

CHECKLIST
- [ ] READ
- [ ] PLAN
- [ ] SOLVE
- [ ] CHECK

Solving Real-World Problems on Coordinate Planes

PLUG IN   Number Lines

You can see how numbers are related to each other on a **number line**.

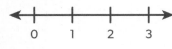

You can **plot** a point on a number line to show a numerical value.

There is a **tic mark** at each number. Start with the tic mark at 0 and count the space between each tic mark: 1, 2, 3.

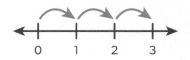

I see! A number line has equally spaced marks named by numbers.

The point is located at 1 on the number line.

I can see on the number line that 0 and 3 are 3 units apart.

Words to Know

number line
a line with equally spaced tic marks representing a set of numbers

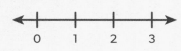

plot
to mark the location of a number with a point

tic mark
a vertical line segment on a number line that stands for a number

tic marks

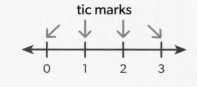

DISCUSS   What are some ways in which number lines are useful in math?

A You can draw a number line.

DO   Draw a number line from 0 to 5.

1 Draw a line.

2 Divide the line equally into 5 segments. Make a tic mark at the beginning of each segment and one at the end.

3 Label the marks beginning with 0 and number them to 5.

184 LESSON 19

B You can plot a point on a number line.

Only the even numbers are labeled, but I can figure out where the odd numbers belong.

DO Plot point *A* at 5 on the number line.

❶ Draw a point on the line at 5.

❷ Label the point.

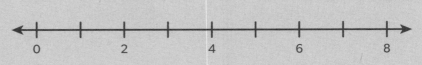

C You can find the distance between two points on a number line.

DO Find the distance between point *A* and point *B*.

❶ Start at 0, or point *A*.

❷ Count the units from point *A* to point *B*. Draw each jump between the numbers.

❸ The number of units is the distance.

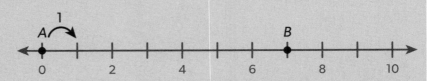

The distance between point *A* and point *B* is _____ units.

PRACTICE

Fill in the numbers to complete the number line.

1

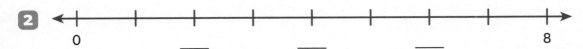

0   **1**   ___   3   ___   ___

2

0   ___   ___   ___   8

Plot point *X* on the number line and find the distance from 0 to *X*.

3 Plot *X* at 6.

0   5   10

The distance from 0 to *X* is _____ units.

4 Plot *X* at 3.

0   5   10

The distance from 0 to *X* is _____ units.

Graphing Ordered Pairs

A **coordinate plane** is a grid formed by a vertical and horizontal line called **axes**.

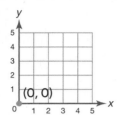

The axes cross at (0, 0), called the **origin**.

I get it! The x-axis goes left and right. The y-axis goes up and down.

You can plot a point using a set of two numbers, called an **ordered pair**.

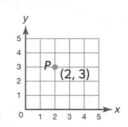

The ordered pair for point P is (2, 3). The first number, 2, is the x-coordinate. The second number, 3, is the y-coordinate.

The first number in an ordered pair tells how many units to count to the right of the origin. The second number tells how many units to count up.

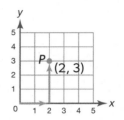

I start at (0, 0) and count 2 units right and 3 units up.

Words to Know

coordinate plane a grid with vertical and horizontal number lines	**axes** the number lines that make up a coordinate plane	**origin** the point (0, 0) on a coordinate plane, where the x-axis and y-axis meet	**ordered pair** a pair of numbers that describes the location of a point on a coordinate plane
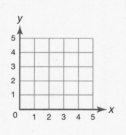	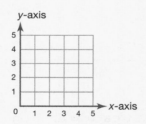	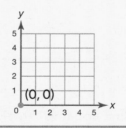	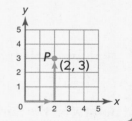

DISCUSS Describe how you would plot the ordered pairs (1, 4) and (4, 1) on a coordinate plane.

A You can name the location of a point on the coordinate plane.

DO Write the ordered pair for point A.

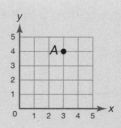

❶ Find the x-coordinate. Count how many units to the right point A is from the origin.

❷ Find the y-coordinate. Count how many units up.

❸ Write the coordinates as an ordered pair.

A: (___3___, _____)

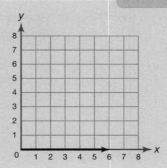

The x-coordinate comes before the y-coordinate—just as X comes before Y in the alphabet!

B You can plot a point on the coordinate plane.

DO

Plot point *B* at (6, 2).

1 Starting at the origin, move right the number of units described by the *x*-coordinate.

2 From there, move up the number of units described by the *y*-coordinate.

3 Plot and label the point.

DISCUSS

Marnel plotted point *M*. He said the coordinates of *M* are (4, 2). What can you tell Marnel about his work?

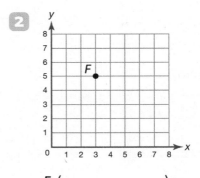

PRACTICE

Name the location of the point.

1

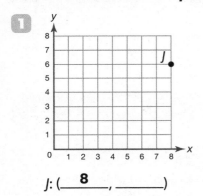

J: (____**8**____, _____)

2

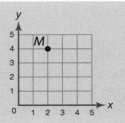

F: (_____, _____)

Plot and label each point on the coordinate plane.

3 *Z*: (2, 7)

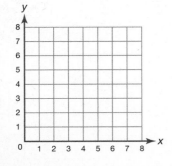

4 *Q*: (5, 0)

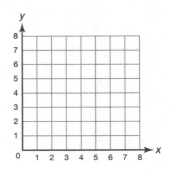

Solving Real-World Problems on Coordinate Planes

A coordinate plane can show the locations of several points.

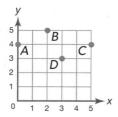

You can follow instructions to plot new points.

Plot point *E* located 1 unit right and 2 units down from point *A*.

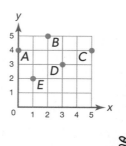

You can also find the distance between two points.

Point *D* is 3 units to the right of point *B*.

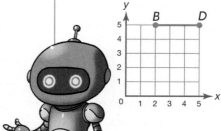

I remember! The first number in the ordered pair is the distance to the right of the origin, and the second numbers is the distance up.

I need to start at the known point, *A*, and move to the right and then down.

I get it! The distance between points *B* and *D* is 3 units.

DISCUSS Chris plotted point *F* at (2, 1). Then he plotted point *G* at (2, 4). What is the distance between point *F* and point *G*?

LESSON LINK

PLUG IN

You can use a number line to show the location of a point and its distance from 0.

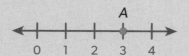

POWER UP

You can use a coordinate plane to show the location of a point and its distance from the origin, (0, 0).

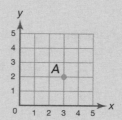

GO!

I get it! I can use the locations of points on coordinate planes to solve problems involving distance.

WORK TOGETHER

You can plot and label points on a coordinate plane.

- Plot point *C*. Start at (0, 0). Move 2 units to the right. Then move 3 units up. Draw and label the point.

- From point *C*, move right 4 units. Plot and label point *D*.

- From point *D*, move up 3 units. Plot and label point *E*.

- From point *E*, move left 4 units. Plot and label point *F*.

Write the ordered pair for each point. Connect the points, and name the shape.

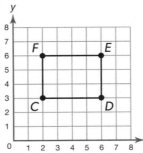

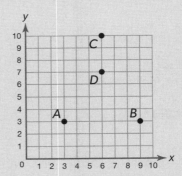

Moving from point to point is like following a path in a game!

Point *C* is located at (2, 3), point *D* is located at (6, 3), point *E* is located at (6, 6), and point *F* is located at (2, 6).

The shape is a rectangle.

Coordinate Grids can be found on p. 245.

A You can find the distance between points on a coordinate plane.

DO The coordinate plane shows the locations of pictures hanging on Kara's wall. Find the distance between pictures *A* and *B*, and between pictures *C* and *D*.

1 Count the units from point *A* to point *B*. Write the distance.

2 Count the units from point *C* to point *D*. Write the distance.

From *A* to *B*, move _____ units to the _____.

A and *B* are _____ units apart.

From *C* to *D*, move _____ units _____.

C and *D* are _____ units apart.

DISCUSS Carson plotted point *S* at (2, 2), point *T* at (2, 7), point *U* at (7, 2) and point *V* at (7, 7). If he connects the points, what shape will he make? What is the distance between each point?

PRACTICE

Plot a point to solve.

1 Vinay plotted 3 points for the corners of a rectangle. Where should he plot a point for the fourth corner, *W*? Plot and label point *W* on the coordinate plane, and name its coordinates.

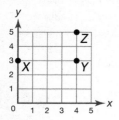

Point *W* is located at (____**0**____, _____).

2 Gary's Gym has a climbing wall with rocks located at the points shown. Gary wants to position one more rock, *R*, that is 2 units left and 3 units up from rock *K*. Plot and label point *R* on the coordinate plane, and name its coordinates.

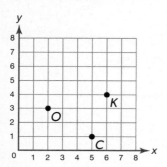

Point *R* is located at (_____, _____).

3 Liz planted a garden as shown. She wants to plant carrots 4 rows right and 1 row up from the onions. Plot and label a point on the coordinate plane where Liz should plant carrots, and name its coordinates.

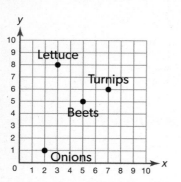

Liz should plant carrots at (____**6**____, _____).

Find the distance to solve.

4 Caden walked from Josh's house to Reagan's house on the map shown. How many blocks did he walk? Each unit is 1 block.

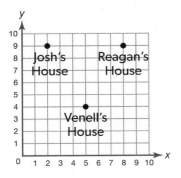

_____ blocks

5 Brody drew a map of some places in his town on the coordinate plane below. What is the distance between the post office and the bank? Each unit is 1 mile.

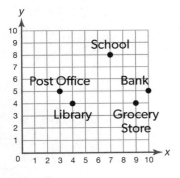

_____ miles

DISCUSS

Construct an Argument

Mrs. Cane drew line segment *L* from (1, 8) to (6, 8) and line segment *M* from (4, 3) to (4, 9). A student says that line segment *L* is longer.

How can you convince the student that line segment *M* is longer?

How long is line segment *L*?

How long is line segment *M*?

PROBLEM SOLVING

IN THE NEIGHBORHOOD

READ

Kay's neighborhood has a library, school, park, and pool. How many blocks does Kay walk to get from the library to the park?

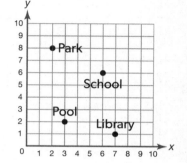

PLAN

• What is the problem asking you to find?

The distance from the _____

to the _____

• What do you need to know to solve this problem?

You need to know the locations of the two places. Each unit on the coordinate plane shows 1 block.

The library is located at (_____, _____).

The park is located at (_____, _____).

• How can you solve the problem?

You can find the number of blocks from the library to the park.

Whether you count up first or left first, you get the same answer!

SOLVE

How many blocks to the left does Kay travel?

Subtract the x-coordinates.

$7 - 2 =$ _____ blocks

How many blocks up does Kay travel?

Subtract the y-coordinates.

_____ − _____ = _____ blocks

How many total blocks does Kay travel? _____ + _____ = _____ blocks

CHECK

You can check your answer by counting the blocks on a different path.

Count units up from the library: _____ blocks

Count units to the left to the park: _____ blocks

The total distance is _____ blocks.

Kay travels _____ blocks from the library to the park.

PRACTICE

Use the problem-solving steps to help you.

1 Trina used a grid to organize her room. Each unit on the grid shows 1 foot. How far is it from Trina's dollhouse to her bookshelf? Count units up and then across.

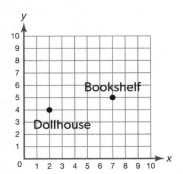

CHECKLIST

☐ READ
☐ PLAN
☐ SOLVE
☐ CHECK

2 The grid shows the locations of several items in a store. How many units apart are the carrots and the milk? Count units across and then down.

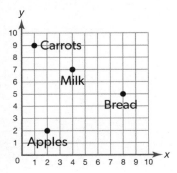

CHECKLIST

☐ READ
☐ PLAN
☐ SOLVE
☐ CHECK

3 The grid shows Mr. Vory's classroom. Each unit is 2 feet. How far is it from Mr. Vory's desk to the sink? Count units across and then down.

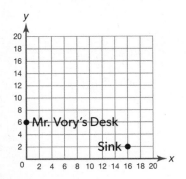

Skip count by 2s to find the distance.

CHECKLIST

☐ READ
☐ PLAN
☐ SOLVE
☐ CHECK

Classifying Two-Dimensional Figures

PLUG IN Points, Lines, Rays, and Angles

Points, lines, rays, and angles are the building blocks of larger figures.

A point is an exact location.

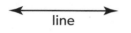
point

A line is straight and continues in both directions.

line

A line segment is a part of a line and has two endpoints.

endpoint   endpoint

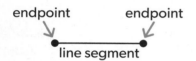
line segment

A ray is a part of a line. It has one endpoint and continues in one direction.

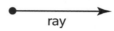
ray

An angle is formed by two rays. Angles can be classified as **acute**, **right**, or **obtuse**.

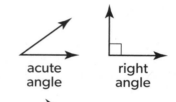
acute angle   right angle

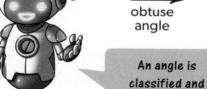
obtuse angle

Parallel lines stay the same distance apart and do not meet. Perpendicular lines meet and form right angles.

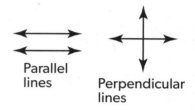
Parallel lines   Perpendicular lines

A square is made up of points, line segments, right angles, parallel line segments, and perpendicular line segments.

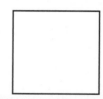

I see! A line segment has two endpoints, but a line continues at both ends.

An angle is classified and named by its size.

I get it! I can use these basic figures to draw other figures.

Words to Know

acute angle
an angle with a measure less than 90°

right angle
an angle with a measure of exactly 90°

obtuse angle
an angle with a measure greater than 90° but less than 180°

DISCUSS Look around your classroom. Name some real-world objects that can be described using the words in the Instruction box above.

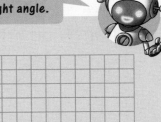

The angle I draw will be less than a right angle.

A You can draw figures on a grid.

DO   Draw an acute angle.

1 An acute angle has a measure less than 90°.

2 Draw a point.

3 Starting from that point, draw a horizontal ray.

4 From the same point, draw a second ray to form an acute angle.

B You can identify the parts of a larger figure.

DO   Identify the parts of this figure.

1 Identify the number of line segments and the number of corners of the parallelogram.

2 Describe the sides.

3 Describe the angles.

The parallelogram has ___**4**___ line segments.

Their endpoints are the ___**4**___ corners of the figure.

The red side is parallel to the _____ side.

The green side is _____ to the blue side.

The parallelogram has two acute angles and

two _____ angles.

PRACTICE

Draw the figure on the grid.

1 line

2 parallel line segments

3 obtuse angle

4 perpendicular lines

You can identify a figure by looking at its **vertices**, its sides, and its angles.

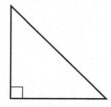

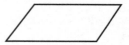

- Count the number of sides and vertices.

  The figure has 3 sides and 3 vertices.

- Look for parallel or perpendicular sides.

  The figure has one pair of perpendicular sides and no parallel sides.

- Look for acute, right, or obtuse angles.

  The figure has one right angle, 2 acute angles, and no obtuse angles.

- Name the figure in different ways.

  It is a two-dimensional figure. It is a **polygon**. It is a triangle. It is a right triangle.

- Count the number of sides and vertices.

  The figure has 4 sides and 4 vertices.

- Look for parallel or perpendicular sides.

  The figure has two pairs of parallel sides and no perpendicular sides.

- Look for acute, right, or obtuse angles.

  The figure has 2 acute angles and 2 obtuse angles. It has no right angles.

- Name the figure in different ways.

  It is a two-dimensional figure. It is a polygon. It is a **quadrilateral**. It is a **parallelogram**.

I can use what I know about angles and parallel and perpendicular sides to identify figures.

I remember! The symbol in the square corner of the triangle means that it is a right angle.

Words to Know	**vertex (vertices)** the point where two sides of an angle meet; the corner of a polygon	**polygon** a two-dimensional figure with three or more straight sides	**quadrilateral** a polygon with 4 sides and 4 angles	**parallelogram** a quadrilateral with 2 pairs of parallel sides

vertex

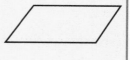

DISCUSS Why can it be helpful to count the numbers of sides and vertices first when identifying two-dimensional figures?

A You can identify a figure by looking at its sides, vertices, and angles.

DO Identify the figure in different ways.

I see! Triangles can be classified in more than one way.

1 Count the number of sides and vertices.

2 Look for acute, right, and obtuse angles.

3 Look at the sides.

The figure has ____3____ sides and ____3____ vertices.

It is a _____.

All of its angles are _____.

So, it is a(n) _____ triangle.

The numbers next to each side show that all

3 sides are _____.

So, it is a(n) _____ triangle, too.

DISCUSS Can you name every triangle in at least two different ways? Explain.

PRACTICE

Name the figure. If possible, name the figure in more than one way.

1

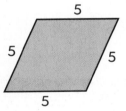

_____

_____

2

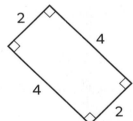

_____

_____

Two-Dimensional Figures can be found on p. 251.

Classify the triangle based on (a) its angle measures, and (b) its side lengths.

3

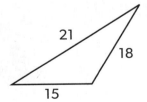

a) _____

b) _____

4

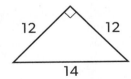

a) _____

b) _____

Classifying Two-Dimensional Figures

Two-dimensional figures can be classified based on their properties.
The concept map shows relationships among the different types of quadrilaterals.

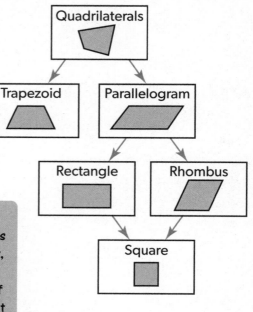

- A trapezoid is the only quadrilateral with exactly one pair of parallel sides.

- A parallelogram is a quadrilateral with two pairs of parallel sides.

- Rectangles, rhombuses, and squares are parallelograms.

- A square is an example of a rectangle and a rhombus.

I get it! If a figure belongs to a category, it has all the properties of figures in that category.

Each figure in the concept map has properties in common with the figure above it.

DISCUSS Do all squares have the same properties as rectangles? Do all rectangles have the same properties as squares? Explain.

LESSON LINK

PLUG IN	POWER UP	GO!

PLUG IN

You can identify angles and parallel and perpendicular line segments in figures.

2 right angles — parallel line segments

POWER UP

You can identify triangles and quadrilaterals based on their sides and their angles.

A trapezoid has 4 angles and 4 sides. It is a quadrilateral with one pair of parallel sides.

GO!

I get it! I can use what I know about two-dimensional figures to understand how triangles and quadrilaterals are classified.

WORK TOGETHER

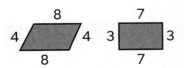

Figures must have "at least" two sides the same length, not "only" two sides the same length.

Use Math Tool: Two-Dimensional Figures to classify figures based on their properties.

- Look at the triangles, classified according to side length. An isosceles triangle and an equilateral triangle each have at least 2 sides the same length.

- Look at the quadrilaterals. A parallelogram, a rectangle, a square, and a rhombus each have at least 2 sides the same length.

Which type of triangle or quadrilateral can be sorted into this group?

Group: at least two sides the same length

An isosceles triangle has at least two sides equal in length.

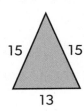

An equilateral triangle is also an isosceles triangle because it has three sides equal in length.

A parallelogram and a rectangle have two pairs of sides the same length.

A square and a rhombus are parallelograms with four sides the same length.

A You can sort figures based on their properties.

DO

Which of these figures can be classified in this group?
Group: at least one pair of perpendicular sides

1 Define *perpendicular*.

2 Review each figure.

3 Look for figures that have at least two sides that meet at a right angle.

Two-Dimensional Figures can be found on p. 251.

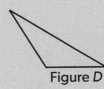

Figure *A*   Figure *B*   Figure *C*   Figure *D*

Perpendicular sides meet at a _____ angle.

Figure _____ is a square. All of its adjacent sides are perpendicular.

Figure _____ is a right triangle. Its vertical side and bottom side are perpendicular.

So, those two figures belong in the group.

The other two figures, _____ and _____, have no right angles. They do not belong in the group.

DISCUSS

Timothy says that all equilateral triangles are also acute triangles. Is his statement true? Explain why or why not.

PRACTICE

List the figures that belong in the group described.

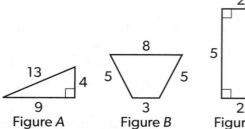

| Figure A | Figure B | Figure C | Figure D | Figure E | Figure F |

1 **Group:** at least one pair of parallel sides

_____

2 **Group:** at least one pair of perpendicular sides

Figures A, _____

> **REMEMBER** Perpendicular sides meet at right angles.

3 **Group:** no sides the same length

_____

4 **Group:** only two sides the same length

_____

Name the group(s) in which each figure belongs.

Group 1: two pairs of parallel sides

Group 2: all sides the same length

Group 3: all right angles

5 parallelogram

Group(s) _____

6 square

Group(s) __**1,**___

> **HINT** A square is a parallelogram.

7 equilateral triangle

Group(s) _____

8 rectangle

Group(s) _____

Complete the concept map for the given terms. Write the term and draw an example in each part of the concept map.

9 Fill in the concept map for Quadrilaterals with *Trapezoid*, *Square*, and *Rhombus*.

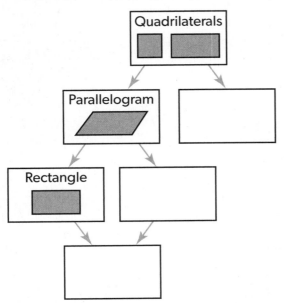

10 Fill in the concept map for Triangles with *Equilateral*, *Isosceles*, and *Scalene*.

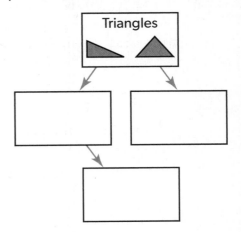

> I know a rhombus and a square each have 4 equal sides. I have to think about their other properties, too.

Write *true* or *false* for each statement.

11 A rhombus has all the properties of a square. _____

12 A square has all the properties of a rhombus. _____

 Is It Possible?

Decide which of the following classifications is possible. If possible, sketch an example. If not possible, explain why not.

a scalene, right triangle | **an isosceles, right triangle** | **an equilateral, right triangle**

PROBLEM SOLVING

WHAT SHAPE IS IT?

READ Lian buys a necklace with a pendant. She says the shape of the pendant is a rectangle. Her mother says it is also a rhombus. If both are correct, what is a third name for the shape?

PLAN
- What is the problem asking you to find?

    A third name for the _____ of the pendant

- What do you need to know to solve the problem?

    The shape is both a rectangle and a _____.

- How can you figure out what the shape of the pendant is?

    I can think about the properties of both of those figures.

SOLVE List the properties of both figures.

- A rectangle is a parallelogram with _____ right angles.
- A rhombus is a parallelogram with all sides _____.

Which parallelogram has angles and sides that match both those descriptions?

A _____ does, because it is both a rectangle and a rhombus.

CHECK The pendant has a _____ shape. Sketch that shape below.

Does the sketch show a rectangle? _____, because _____.

Does the sketch show a rhombus? _____, because _____.

A third name for the shape of the pendant is a _____.

Use Math Tool: Two-Dimensional Figures on page 251 to help you.

PRACTICE

Use the problem-solving steps to help you.

1 The shape of a tabletop is a quadrilateral with only one pair of perpendicular sides. What are the possible shapes of the tabletop? Explain your reasoning.

CHECKLIST
- [ ] READ
- [ ] PLAN
- [ ] SOLVE
- [ ] CHECK

2 A logo for a pizza parlor is shaped like an equilateral triangle. What are two other ways you can classify the shape of the logo?

CHECKLIST
- [ ] READ
- [ ] PLAN
- [ ] SOLVE
- [ ] CHECK

3 An architect drew blueprints for a new playground. The shape of the playground is a parallelogram that is not a square. What are the possible shapes of the playground?

CHECKLIST
- [ ] READ
- [ ] PLAN
- [ ] SOLVE
- [ ] CHECK

Glossary

acute angle an angle with a measure less than 90° (Lesson 20)

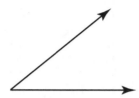

acute triangle a triangle with all angles less than 90° (Lesson 20)

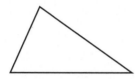

area the size of a two-dimensional figure in square units (Lessons 11, 18)

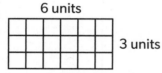

Area = 18 square units

area model a model that shows the size of a surface in square units (Lesson 5)

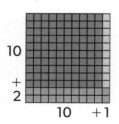

$10 \times 10 = 100$

$1 \times 10 = 10$

$10 \times 2 = 20$

$1 \times 2 = 2$

$100 + 10 + 20 + 2 = 132$

The product of 11×12 is 132.

axes the number lines that make up a coordinate plane (Lesson 19)

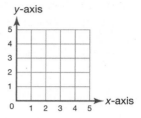

base any face of a rectangular prism (Lesson 18)

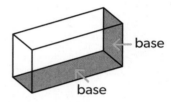

base number a number that is multiplied by itself a certain number of times (Lesson 2)

coordinate plane a grid formed by a horizontal line called the *x*-axis and a vertical line called the *y*-axis (Lesson 19)

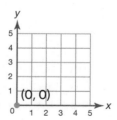

cubic centimeter a unit cube with a side length of 1 centimeter (Lesson 17)

cubic foot a unit cube with a side length of 1 foot (Lesson 17)

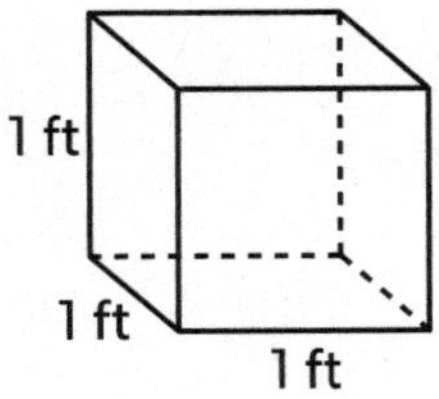

cubic inch a unit cube with a side length of 1 inch (Lesson 17)

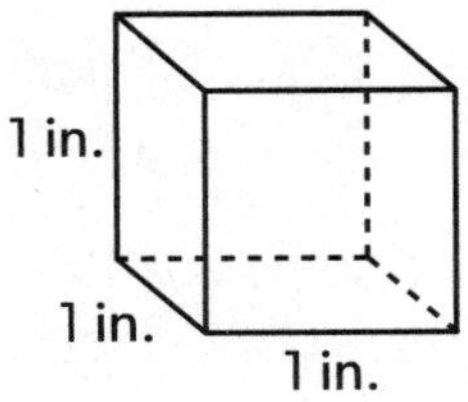

cubic unit a cube with an edge length of 1 of any given unit (Lesson 17)

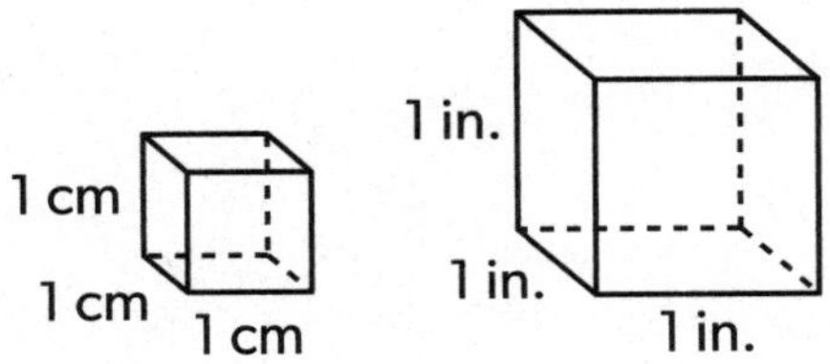

customary system of measurement the system of units of measure used in the United States (Lesson 15)

measures of length: inches, feet, yards

decimal a number with a decimal point (Lessons 3, 7)

78.309

decimal point (.) a symbol that separates the whole number from the fractional part in a number (Lessons 2, 7)

12.34
↑
decimal point

denominator the bottom number in a fraction; tells how many equal parts there are (Lessons 8, 9, 11)

$\frac{1}{\mathbf{4}}$ ← denominator

dividend a number to be divided (Lessons 6, 9)

$6\overline{)420}$ = 70 ← dividend

divisor the number by which the dividend is divided (Lessons 6, 9, 14)

divisor → $6\overline{)420}$ = 70

equation a number sentence that shows that the values on both side of the equal (=) sign are the same (Lesson 13)

$$7 \times \frac{1}{3} = \frac{7}{3}$$

equilateral triangle a triangle with all sides the same length (Lesson 20)

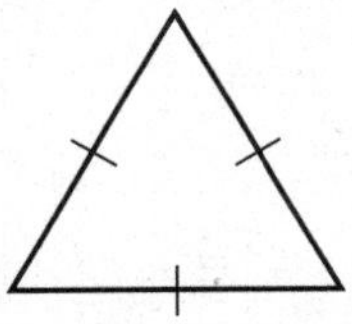

equivalent fractions two or more fractions that name the same value but have different numerators and denominators (Lesson 8)

$$\frac{1}{4} = \frac{2}{8} = \frac{3}{12}$$

expanded form a way of writing a number as a sum of the values of its digits (Lesson 3)

406,285 in expanded form is
400,000 + 6,000 + 200 + 80 + 5

exponent a number that tells how many times a given number is used as a factor (Lesson 2)

$$10^4$$

↑
exponent

faces the flat surfaces of a solid figure (Lesson 17)

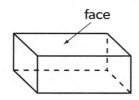

face

factor a number that is multiplied to get a product (Lessons 5, 6)

formula a special type of equation that shows a mathematical relationship (Lessons 11, 18)

Area = length × width

$A = l \times w$

hundredth one of one hundred equal parts; $\frac{1}{100}$ (Lesson 3)

improper fraction a fraction with a numerator that is greater than or equal to the denominator (Lessons 8, 12, 13, 16)

$\frac{5}{5}$ and $\frac{9}{5}$ are improper fractions.

isosceles triangle a triangle with at least two sides the same length (Lesson 20)

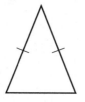

line plot a graph that uses Xs above a number line to record data (Lesson 16)

Plant Growth (in feet)

metric system of measurement the system of units of measure most commonly used throughout the world (Lesson 15)

measures of length: centimeters, meters, kilometers

mixed number a number with a whole-number part and a fraction part (Lessons 8, 13, 14, 16)

$2\frac{1}{4}$ and $7\frac{5}{8}$ are mixed numbers

multiple the product of any two whole numbers (Lessons 9, 10)

$$2 \times \frac{1}{8} = \frac{2}{8}$$
$$3 \times \frac{1}{8} = \frac{3}{8}$$
$$4 \times \frac{1}{8} = \frac{4}{8}$$

$\frac{2}{8}$, $\frac{3}{8}$, and $\frac{4}{8}$ are all multiples of $\frac{1}{8}$.

20 is a multiple of 2 and a multiple of 10

multiple of 10 a product of 10 and another number (Lesson 2)

$$2 \times 10 = 20$$
$$3 \times 10 = 30$$
$$4 \times 10 = 40$$

20, 30, and 40 are multiples of 10.

number line a line divided into equally-spaced segments and labeled with numbers (Lesson 19)

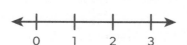

numerator the top number in a fraction; tells how many equal parts are being considered (Lessons 8, 9, 11)

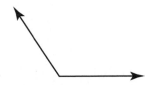

numerator $\rightarrow \dfrac{1}{4}$

obtuse angle an angle with a measure greater than 90° but less than 180° (Lesson 20)

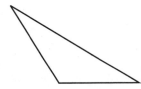

obtuse triangle a triangle with one obtuse angle (Lesson 20)

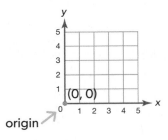

ordered pair two numbers that give a location on a coordinate plane (Lessons 1, 19)

(2, 3)

origin the point (0, 0), on a coordinate plane, where the *x*-axis and *y*-axis meet (Lessons 1, 19)

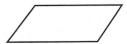

parallelogram a quadrilateral with 2 pairs of parallel sides (Lesson 20)

partial product the result of multiplying one part of one factor by a second factor (Lesson 6)

$$\begin{array}{r} 1\,1 \\ \times\, 1\,2 \\ \hline 2\,2 \\ +\,1\,1\,0 \\ \hline 1\,3\,2 \end{array}$$ ← partial ← products

partial quotient the value of part of a quotient, or the value of one digit in a quotient (Lesson 6)

In 272 ÷ 8 = 34,
30 and 4 are partial quotients.

place value the value of a digit based on its position in a number (Lesson 2)

Tens	Ones
6	2

6 tens and 2 ones: 62

plot to mark the location of a number with a point (Lesson 19)

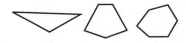

polygon a two-dimensional figure with three or more straight sides (Lesson 20)

power of 10 a number that is the result of multiplying 10 by itself a certain number of times (Lesson 2)

$$10 \times 10 = 100$$

$$10 \times 10 \times 10 = 1{,}000$$

product the result of multiplying two or more numbers (Lessons 2, 5, 6)

$$3 \times 50 = 150$$
$$\uparrow$$
product

quadrilateral a polygon with 4 sides and 4 angles (Lesson 20)

quotient the result of division (Lessons 6, 9)

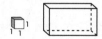

reciprocal one of two numbers whose product is 1 (Lesson 14)

$$4 \text{ and } \tfrac{1}{4} \text{ are reciprocals: } 4 \times \tfrac{1}{4} = 1$$

rectangle a parallelogram with 4 right angles (Lesson 20)

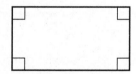

rectangular prism a solid figure with faces that are rectangles (Lessons 17, 18)

remainder the number that is left over after division is complete (Lessons 6, 14)

rhombus a parallelogram with 4 equal sides (Lesson 20)

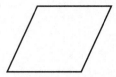

right angle an angle with a measure of exactly 90° (Lesson 20)

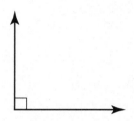

right triangle a triangle with one right angle (Lesson 20)

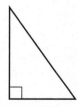

rule tells how the numbers in a pattern are related (Lesson 1)

4, 8, 12, 16

The rule is *add 4*.

scalene triangle a triangle with all sides different length (Lesson 20)

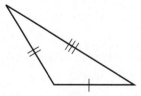

square a parallelogram with 4 right angles and 4 equal sides (Lesson 20)

square unit a unit used to measure the area of a plane figure (Lessons 11, 18)

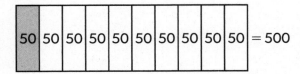

1 unit

1 unit

tenth one of ten equal parts; $\frac{1}{10}$ (Lesson 3)

| 50 | 50 | 50 | 50 | 50 | 50 | 50 | 50 | 50 | 50 | = 500

term a number or figure in a pattern (Lesson 1)

4, 8, 12, 16

The numbers 4, 8, 12, and 16 are all terms in the pattern.

thousandth one of one thousand equal parts; $\frac{1}{1,000}$ (Lesson 3)

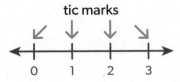

tic mark a vertical line segment on a number line that stands for a number (Lesson 19)

tic marks

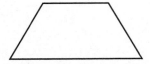

0   1   2   3

trapezoid a quadrilateral with exactly one pair of parallel sides (Lesson 20)

unit cube a cube with a side length of 1 unit and a volume of 1 cubic unit (Lesson 17)

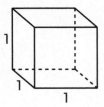

1

1

1

unit fraction a fraction with 1 as the numerator (Lessons 9, 10, 14)

$\frac{1}{10}$ ← numerator of 1

variable a letter or symbol used to represent a number (Lesson 13)

$1\frac{1}{2} \times \frac{1}{3} = n$

↑ variable

vertex the point where two sides of an angle meet; the corner of a polygon (Lesson 20)

vertex

volume the number of cubic units needed to fill a three-dimensional figure (Lessons 17, 18)

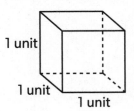

1 unit

1 unit

1 unit

1 cubic unit of volume

x-coordinate tells how many units to move to the right along the x-axis (Lesson 1)

(**2**, 3)

y-coordinate tells how many units to move up along the y-axis (Lesson 1)

(2, **3**)

Math Tool: Grid Paper

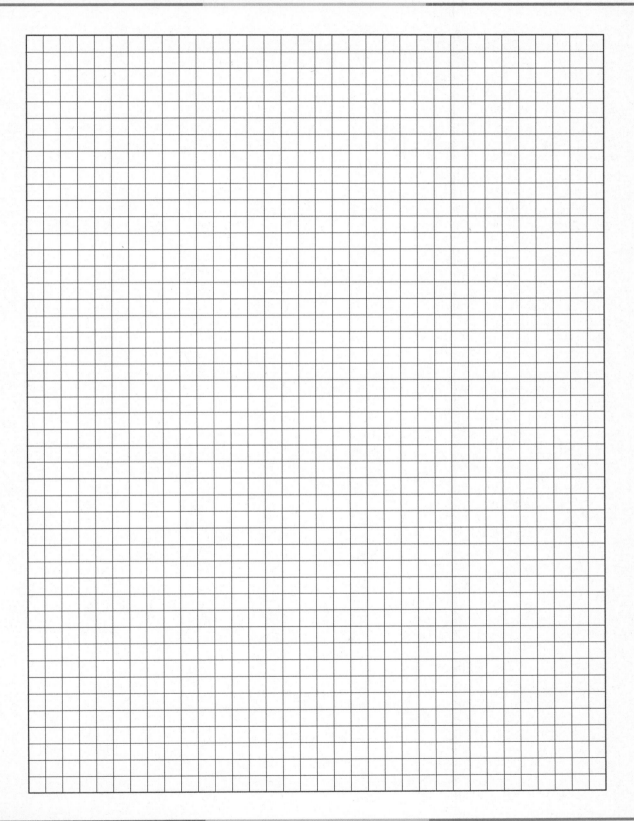

Name _____ Date _____

Math Tool: Grid Paper

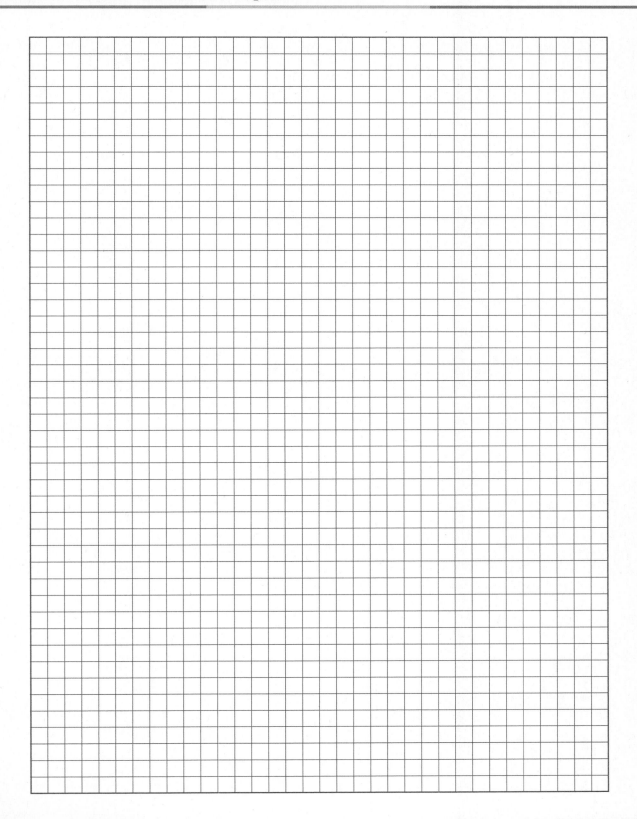

Math Tool: Decimal Place-Value Chart

Thousandths					
Hundredths					
Tenths					
Decimal Point					
Ones					
Tens					

Thousandths					
Hundredths					
Tenths					
Decimal Point					
Ones					
Tens					

Math Tool: Decimal Place-Value Chart

Tens	Ones	Decimal Point	Tenths	Hundredths	Thousandths

Tens	Ones	Decimal Point	Tenths	Hundredths	Thousandths

Name _____ Date _____

Math Tool: Decimal Place-Value Chart

Thousandths	Hundredths	Tenths	Decimal Point	Ones	Tens

Thousandths	Hundredths	Tenths	Decimal Point	Ones	Tens

Math Tool: Decimal Place-Value Chart

Thousandths	Hundredths	Tenths	Decimal Point	Ones	Tens

Thousandths	Hundredths	Tenths	Decimal Point	Ones	Tens

Math Tool: Decimal Place-Value Chart

Tens	Ones	Decimal Point	Tenths	Hundredths	Thousandths

Tens	Ones	Decimal Point	Tenths	Hundredths	Thousandths

Math Tool: Decimal Place-Value Chart

Tens	Ones	Decimal Point	Tenths	Hundredths	Thousandths

Tens	Ones	Decimal Point	Tenths	Hundredths	Thousandths

Math Tool: Grids

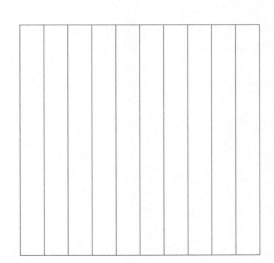
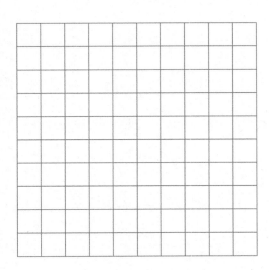
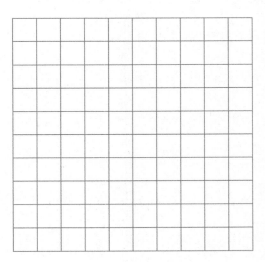

Math Tool: Grids

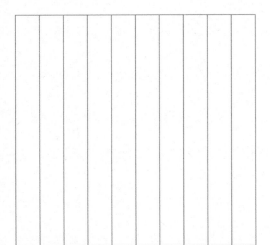
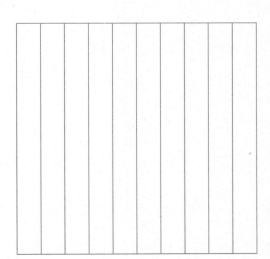
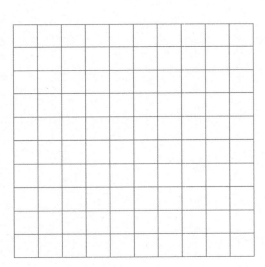
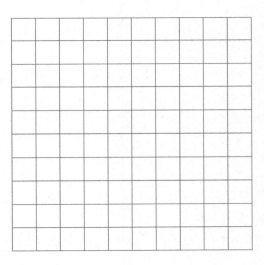

Math Tool: Grids

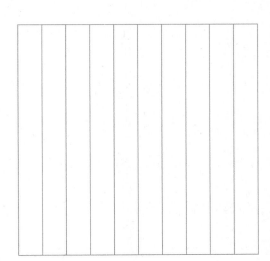
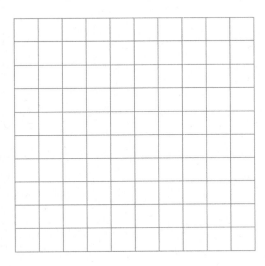
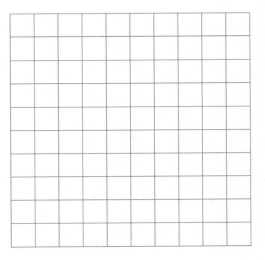

Math Tool: Grids

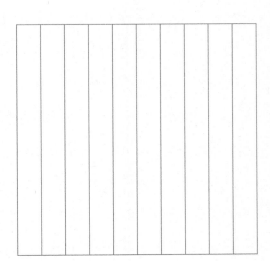

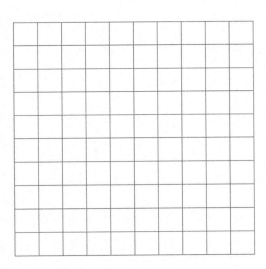
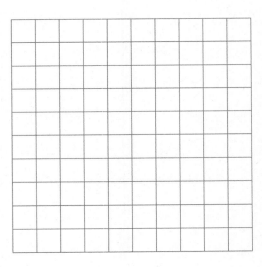

Math Tool: Fraction Strips

1

$\frac{1}{2}$	$\frac{1}{2}$

$\frac{1}{3}$	$\frac{1}{3}$	$\frac{1}{3}$

$\frac{1}{4}$	$\frac{1}{4}$	$\frac{1}{4}$	$\frac{1}{4}$

$\frac{1}{5}$	$\frac{1}{5}$	$\frac{1}{5}$	$\frac{1}{5}$	$\frac{1}{5}$

$\frac{1}{6}$	$\frac{1}{6}$	$\frac{1}{6}$	$\frac{1}{6}$	$\frac{1}{6}$	$\frac{1}{6}$

$\frac{1}{8}$	$\frac{1}{8}$	$\frac{1}{8}$	$\frac{1}{8}$	$\frac{1}{8}$	$\frac{1}{8}$	$\frac{1}{8}$	$\frac{1}{8}$

$\frac{1}{10}$	$\frac{1}{10}$	$\frac{1}{10}$	$\frac{1}{10}$	$\frac{1}{10}$	$\frac{1}{10}$	$\frac{1}{10}$	$\frac{1}{10}$	$\frac{1}{10}$	$\frac{1}{10}$

$\frac{1}{12}$	$\frac{1}{12}$	$\frac{1}{12}$	$\frac{1}{12}$	$\frac{1}{12}$	$\frac{1}{12}$	$\frac{1}{12}$	$\frac{1}{12}$	$\frac{1}{12}$	$\frac{1}{12}$	$\frac{1}{12}$	$\frac{1}{12}$

Math Tool: Fraction Strips

1

| $\frac{1}{2}$ | $\frac{1}{2}$ |

| $\frac{1}{3}$ | $\frac{1}{3}$ | $\frac{1}{3}$ |

| $\frac{1}{4}$ | $\frac{1}{4}$ | $\frac{1}{4}$ | $\frac{1}{4}$ |

| $\frac{1}{5}$ | $\frac{1}{5}$ | $\frac{1}{5}$ | $\frac{1}{5}$ | $\frac{1}{5}$ |

| $\frac{1}{6}$ | $\frac{1}{6}$ | $\frac{1}{6}$ | $\frac{1}{6}$ | $\frac{1}{6}$ | $\frac{1}{6}$ |

| $\frac{1}{8}$ | $\frac{1}{8}$ | $\frac{1}{8}$ | $\frac{1}{8}$ | $\frac{1}{8}$ | $\frac{1}{8}$ | $\frac{1}{8}$ | $\frac{1}{8}$ |

| $\frac{1}{10}$ | $\frac{1}{10}$ | $\frac{1}{10}$ | $\frac{1}{10}$ | $\frac{1}{10}$ | $\frac{1}{10}$ | $\frac{1}{10}$ | $\frac{1}{10}$ | $\frac{1}{10}$ | $\frac{1}{10}$ |

| $\frac{1}{12}$ | $\frac{1}{12}$ | $\frac{1}{12}$ | $\frac{1}{12}$ | $\frac{1}{12}$ | $\frac{1}{12}$ | $\frac{1}{12}$ | $\frac{1}{12}$ | $\frac{1}{12}$ | $\frac{1}{12}$ | $\frac{1}{12}$ | $\frac{1}{12}$ |

Math Tool: Fraction Models

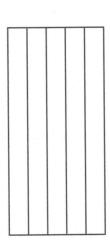
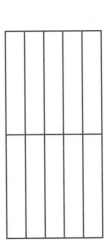

Name _____   Date _____

Math Tool: Fraction Models

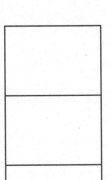

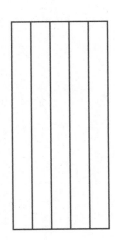
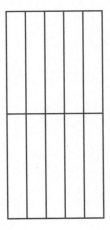

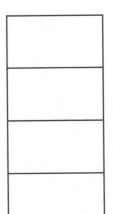

Name _____ Date _____

Math Tool: Fraction Models

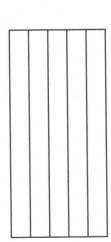
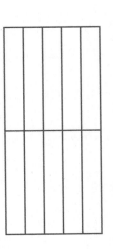
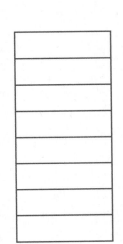

Math Tool: Coordinate Grids

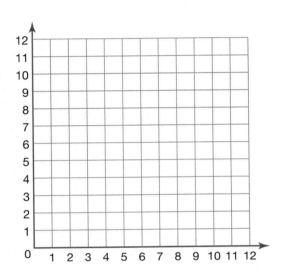

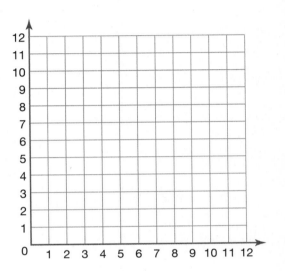

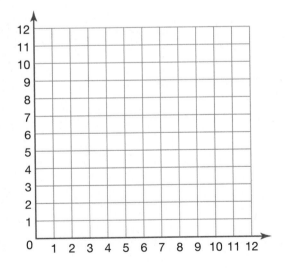

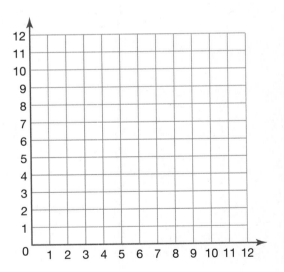

Math Tool: Coordinate Grids

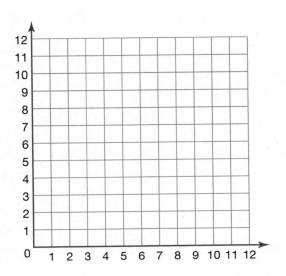

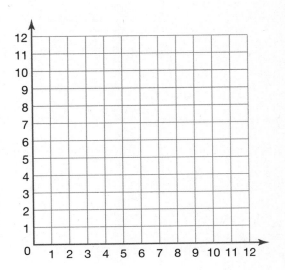

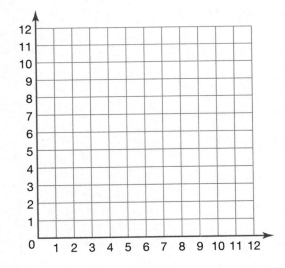

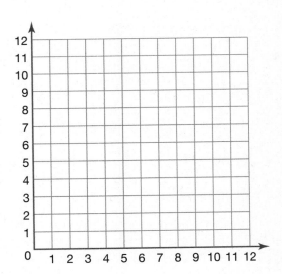

Math Tool: Customary and Metric Units

Customary Units of Length

1 foot (ft) = 12 inches (in.)

1 yard (yd) = 3 feet (ft)

1 yard (yd) = 36 inches (in.)

1 mile (mi) = 5,280 feet (ft)

Metric Units of Length

1 centimeter (cm) = 10 millimeters (mm)

1 meter (m) = 100 centimeters (cm)

1 kilometer (km) = 1,000 meters (m)

Customary Units of Weight

1 pound (lb) = 16 ounces (oz)

1 ton (T) = 2,000 pounds (lb)

Metric Units of Mass

1 kilogram (kg) = 1,000 grams (g)

Customary Units of Capacity

1 gallon (gal) = 4 quarts (qt)

1 quart (qt) = 2 pints (pt)

1 pint (pt) = 2 cups (c)

1 cup (c) = 8 fluid ounces (fl oz)

Metric Units of Capacity

1 liter (L) = 1,000 milliliters (mL)

Time

1 hour (hr) = 60 minutes (min)

1 minute (min) = 60 seconds (sec)

Math Tool: Two-Dimensional Figures

Triangles

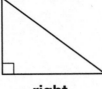

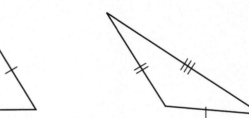

acute
all angles less
than 90°

right
one right angle

obtuse
one obtuse angle

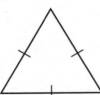

isosceles
at least two sides
equal lengths

equilateral
all sides
equal lengths

scalene
all sides
different length

Quadrilaterals

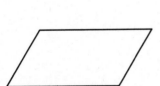

parallelogram
2 pairs of parallel
and equal, opposite
sides

rectangle
parallelogram with
4 right angles

square
parallelogram with
4 right angles and
4 equal sides

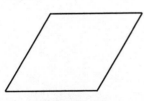

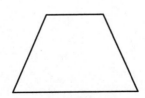

rhombus
parallelogram with
4 equal sides

trapezoid
exactly one pair of
parallel sides

Math Tool: Whole Number Place-Value Chart

Hundred Thousands	Ten Thousands	Thousands	Hundreds	Tens	Ones

Hundred Thousands	Ten Thousands	Thousands	Hundreds	Tens	Ones

Math Tool: Place-Value Models

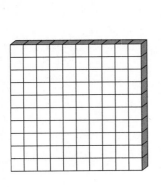

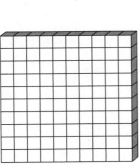

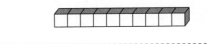

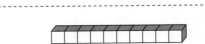

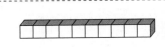

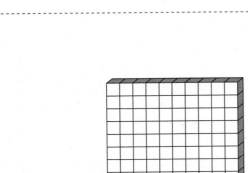

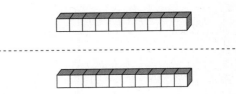

Math Tool: Counters

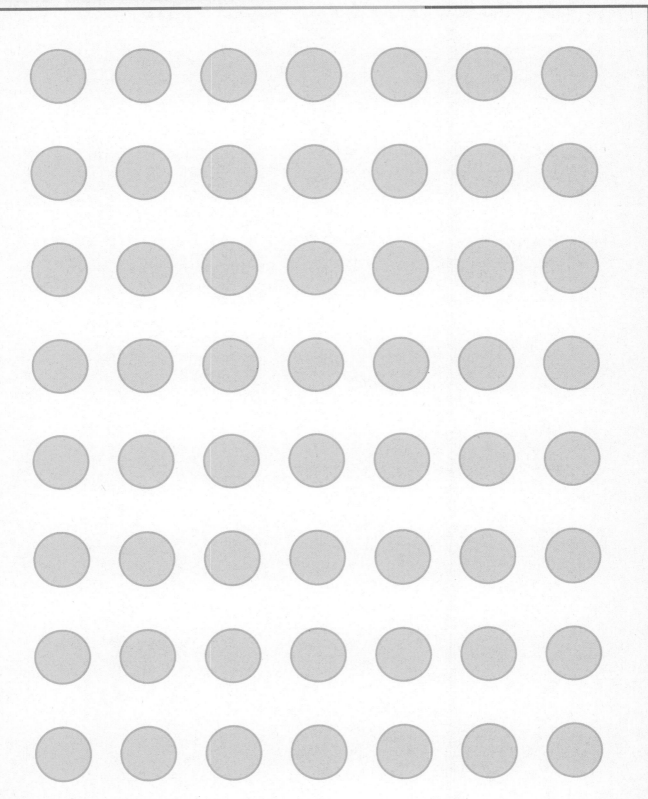

Notes

Notes

Notes

Notes

Notes

Notes

Notes

Notes

Notes

Notes

Notes

Notes

Notes

Notes